The Tanglewood Wedding Shop

LILAC MILLS

The Tanglewood Wedding Shop

CANELO

First published in the United Kingdom in 2020 by Canelo

Canelo Digital Publishing Limited
31 Helen Road
Oxford OX2 0DF
United Kingdom

A CIP catalogue record for this book is available from the British Library.

Print ISBN 978 1 78863 988 0
Ebook ISBN 978 1 78863 833 3

Look for more great books at www.canelo.co

Printed and bound in Great Britain by Clays Ltd, Elcograf S.p.A.

2

Chapter 1

'Can I have a dog?' Danny, who was sitting on the floor playing with Lego, looked up at his mum hopefully.

Edie took a pin out of her mouth and sighed. 'Danny, you know the landlord doesn't allow pets. Besides, I haven't got the time to look after a dog.'

'I've got the time,' her son said earnestly.

'Even if Eastern Estates allowed pets, Dan, you're not old enough to walk a dog on your own.'

Edie shuddered at the thought of her eight-year-old unaccompanied son walking along the river path. Only last year, the river had broken its banks and flooded those cottages which ran alongside it, and everyone who lived in them had to be evacuated. Dangerous things, were rivers.

'How about a kitty?' he suggested. 'Cats don't need to be walked.'

Bless him, he was trying. 'Sorry, Danny, but I can't risk a cat's claws spagging the fabric.' She gestured to the mountain of lace and silk covering the little table in the living room. At any given time, Edie was working on at least three expensive wedding or bridesmaid dresses.

'You could keep them in your room, and keep the door shut. I'll make sure the cat doesn't even go in there.'

'Cats get everywhere, Dan. You can't stop them. You know how I like to keep my bedroom window slightly ajar.'

'I could stop it,' he said, nodding his head vigorously. 'Mary would be a house cat, and never go outside, so you could open your window and she'd never be able to crawl in.'

'Mary? You've given the cat a name?' she asked, and to her surprise, Danny blushed to the roots of his sandy-blond hair.

He bent his head, concentrating on his Lego, and muttered, 'Might have.'

Edie smiled. 'What if it's a boy?'

'It won't be.' Her son was adamant. 'Mary is a girl.'

'There's someone called Mary in your class, isn't there?'

A pause. 'Yes…' He was still muttering, and the blush had developed into two sploshes of bright pink, one on each cheek.

Edie suspected her little boy had a crush. Aww, how sweet; his first one. She slipped an incredibly sharp, fine pin into the white silk, following a faint line of tailor's chalk, unprepared for the sudden rush of wistfulness that hit her. Her son was growing up far too fast; he wouldn't be a child for much longer and then where would she be? He would abandon her for his friends and girls, preferring their company to hers, leaving her all alone with just her job for company and an imaginary cat called Mary.

'If we were allowed to have a dog, would you have called it Mary, too?' she asked.

'Yes.'

'What about…?' She pretended to think. 'A hamster.'

Danny paused, then gave a bent-headed nod, his gaze firmly on his bricks.

'A rabbit?'

Another nod.

'A goldfish?'

'Yep.'

'A chicken?'

'You can't keep chickens inside,' he said, giving her a quick glance. 'Everyone knows they scratch about in gardens and stuff.'

Edie was pretty sure that not everyone knew that little nugget of information, because, unlike his best friend Jack, not many people actually had chickens in their gardens. She smiled.

'OK, how about a parrot?'

'A parrot called Mary? Now you're being silly,' her son declared. 'Parrots are called Polly.'

'They are?'

His nod was emphatic.

'A sheep, then?' she suggested.

He gave her a withering glare.

'Donkey?'

More glaring.

'I know!' She clapped her hands. 'A goat! I like goats.'

'I prefer puppies and kittens,' he said solemnly. 'So, can we?'

Edie sobered, her smile fading. 'I'm sorry, Dan, you know we can't. We've discussed this before.'

'Miss Harding says discussions are when everyone gets to have their say.' Danny stuck out his chin, treating her to his defiant look.

Edie knew his class had started a 'discussion group', to help the pupils with their reasoning skills, and she wondered where this conversation was going.

'Saying "no" isn't a discussion,' Danny added.

He had a point, Edie thought, proud of his burgeoning debating skills. 'The answer is still no,' she said gently, and winced as he thumped a small fist down on the figure he'd been making, breaking it apart. Was his attitude a remnant of toddler tantrums, or the start of teenage angst, she wondered. It wasn't like her normally sweet and gentle son to show a flash of temper.

'If you've finished playing with your Lego, please put it away,' she said mildly, not wanting to let Danny know his irritation had unsettled her.

'It's not fair,' she heard him mutter under his breath, and she had to agree with him. It wasn't fair. A child *should* be able to have a pet, but her work and their landlord made it impossible.

'I agree,' she said, 'but life often isn't fair, Danny.'

He was old enough now to begin to realise the truth of what she'd just said. Although she'd love to keep him as innocent and naive as she possibly could, it wouldn't do him any favours in the long run to shield him from everything. She wanted him to grow up with a certain amount of resilience, to be able to deal with the obstacles life would undoubtedly throw in his path. Making him understand that sometimes a reasonable request had to be refused because of circumstances outside their control was part of that.

Edie stared at the half-formed dress in front of her and sighed. She loved designing and making wedding dresses, and seeing the joy on the faces of the brides, but she wished it paid a bit better. Enough that she could afford to move out of this little rented cottage and buy a house of their own.

Although owning her own home wouldn't alleviate Edie's other problem – that of time. Edie Adams simply didn't have enough of it. She spent every waking hour when she wasn't taking care of Danny working on her wedding dresses. Technically, they weren't hers. They belonged to Mrs Carrington, who owned Moira's Wedding Shop, but Edie felt as though they were hers. She was the one who, together with the bride, brought a dress to glorious life – from a bolt of cloth on a shelf to a beautiful gown fit for a princess. Edie helped make dreams come true, and she loved her job. Mostly.

Mrs Carrington could be hard to please at times. OK, make that most of the time. The woman was grumpy and very difficult to get along with, but Edie had worked for her since shortly after Danny was born, and she was used to her now. However, familiarity didn't always make things any easier when it came to dealing with her boss.

But she didn't have a great deal of choice when it came to jobs. This one was right on her doorstep – literally, because the shop was on the other side of the little court-yard from her cottage – and there weren't many other jobs out there that she could do from the comfort of her own home.

Danny, bless him, had recovered from his fit of pique at not being allowed a pet, and was obediently putting his Lego bricks back in the tub.

'If you give me half an hour to finish pinning this together,' Edie said, 'we'll pop along the high street and get some cakes for after our tea.'

'Yay!' Danny clapped his hands together. 'Can I have a custard slice?'

'If they've got any left,' Edie said. The time was getting on a bit, and the baker didn't usually have an awful lot left by the end of the afternoon. But what cakes he did have left, he often sold off at reduced price, just to get rid of them, and Edie well knew that every penny saved helped their meagre finances.

Danny shot her a look from underneath a lowered brow. 'If you give me some money, I could go now,' he said.

Edie froze.

This was the first time her son had suggested walking to the bakers on his own. It was bound to happen sooner or later, she thought; it was the inevitable and unstoppable drive towards independence, but she wasn't ready for it yet. Danny was only eight (nearly nine, as he kept reminding her). He was far too young to walk along the high street on his own, even if it was only around the corner and up a bit. There were too many people, too many cars; he wasn't nearly ready for such a big step. *She* wasn't ready for it. She'd look at it again when he was a bit older. Like fourteen.

'You're not quite old enough to go on your own,' she said.

'When will I be?' he demanded.

She could tell that he wasn't being awkward or cheeky. He genuinely wanted to know. 'Not for a while, love,' she said.

'Jack is allowed, and he lives in West Street.'

Hmm. Edie frowned. Jack's mother allowed her boy to do far too much, in Edie's opinion. He was even permitted

6

to walk to school on his own, which meant crossing what could sometimes be a busy road at certain times of the day.

'Can we go now?' Danny asked. She could tell he was itching to be outside and doing something more interesting than being cooped up in their little living room with his mother.

'In half an hour,' she repeated.

'You said that half an hour ago.' Danny sighed. 'I'm bored.'

'It's only been five minutes. Why don't you get your paints out?' she suggested.

Ever since he'd gone on a visit into the Beacons with his teacher and one of the park rangers to do some painting, and discovered he was pretty good at it, he'd been happy to sit at his little desk with the lift-up easel. It was getting too small for him now, and he could do with sitting at the table, but most of the time that was covered with metres of silk, satin and tulle, and Edie knew very well that wedding dress fabric and children's paint wasn't a good combination.

'There's nothing to paint,' her son stated.

'What about the apples in the bowl? They're a lovely, shiny red.'

'I want to paint outside,' he said.

'OK, then, how about the flowers in the tubs on the yard?'

They didn't have a garden as such, but they did have a small, pretty yard which Edie had filled with pots and tubs. There was just enough room for a wooden table and a couple of chairs, and not much else.

'Don't want to.' Danny was starting to become sullen.

It was happening more and more often lately, and she realised to her intense sorrow that he was starting to outgrow her.

Once upon a time, she had been his whole world, but not now. His world had irrevocably expanded the second he'd started nursery school and had been expanding exponentially ever since. One day soon, she would be nothing more than a distant little speck on his horizon as he raced towards adulthood.

And then what would she do? Apart from her mum, who she was close to and saw most days, there was no one else in Edie's life, except for her son.

Chapter 2

'It'll be your turn next, mate.' William thumped James on the arm.

'That's hardly likely, is it?' he retorted with a laugh. 'I don't even have a girlfriend.'

'You're too picky.'

'I'm too poor. They see me knocking about with you and think my bank balance is in the same league as yours. When they find out it's not, they soon back off.'

'I'm not exactly rich,' William protested.

'No?' James gazed pointedly around The Manor's grand entrance hall. It was twice the size of the living room in his recently purchased semi-derelict farmhouse. Hell, even the loo off the scullery in The Manor was bigger than his living room.

'I mean, my bank account is probably emptier than yours,' William said.

James gave him an incredulous look. 'Don't you believe it. I've got about three pounds fifty to my name now that I've paid the roofer.'

This little smallholding of his was costing him a fortune, but as far as he was concerned, it was the best (and most expensive) purchase he'd ever made.

'It's good to have you back in the country, James.' William thumped him on the arm again.

James took it as a sign of affection. 'It's good to be back.'

'Did you learn anything useful while you were away, or have the past two years been one long holiday?'

'Cheeky git! I'll have you know I've been working my socks off.'

'Swanning around the USA, you mean,' William said with a laugh, then sobered. 'So, how do you think it went?'

James had been working with several of America's big national parks on the reintroduction of wolves. William was working on a similar project in the UK, but with beavers, not wolves.

'Having an apex predator has made a huge difference in re-establishing balance,' James began. 'They've had a remarkable impact on the whole ecosystem. It's a pity we can't do it in Britain. Talking of which, how's the beaver reintroduction project going?' James had heard that William's father, Lord Tonbridge, had given some land over to beavers a while back.

'It's already starting to help with flooding,' William said, 'slowing the rate of flow from the stream into the river. If we had more beaver dams on the tributaries, then the river might never flood again.'

'Yeah, I heard about that, too. Didn't those cottages by the bridge get flooded out?'

William nodded. 'Three feet deep at the highest point.'

'There you are!' a female voice called, and James looked around to see a pretty girl in a wheelchair coming into the hall.

'Tia,' he said. 'Looking as lovely as ever.'

'Yes, you can have some lemon drizzle cake,' she responded with a wide smile. 'That's what you've come for, isn't it? Tea and cake?'

'Oh, well, if you're offering,' he said. 'William tells me the wedding plans are ticking along nicely.'

Tia grimaced and glanced over her shoulder. 'If you can call butting heads with your future mother-in-law every five minutes "nice". We can't seem to agree on anything.'

'If I can do anything to help…' James offered.

'Just make sure William turns up on time,' she laughed. 'Oh, and whatever you do, don't forget the ring.'

'I won't,' he promised.

'Can I borrow my fiancé this afternoon?' she asked. 'We have to have a cake sampling session.'

James's ears pricked up. 'That sounds fantastic. Can I come?'

'No. Eat your lemon drizzle and behave yourself,' William said. 'Your turn to be involved will come when you help me get fitted for a suit.'

'That's hardly in the same league as cake testing, is it?' James retorted. Though if he kept on popping into The Manor for mid-afternoon refreshments, he'd need to go on a diet soon.

'James, how absolutely wonderful to see you,' Lady Tonbridge trilled, holding both hands out as she glided across the marbled hall towards him.

'Hello, Julia,' James said, taking them in his own and kissing her on the cheek.

'You're back for good, then?' she asked, and he nodded.

'Yep, he bought the old Hopkins place,' William told her.

11

Julia gave a little shudder. 'I thought it was uninhabitable?'

'Almost. It's better now I've put a new roof on; at least it's stopped leaking,' James told her.

'And how is your darling mother?' Julia asked.

'She's good, thanks. Glad to have me home.' Although home for him was Tanglewood and home for his parents was currently Kent. But at least he was in the same country as them and visiting wouldn't now involve a transatlantic flight.

'I expect she is. Give her my love, won't you?' Julia turned to her son and his future bride. 'Now, William and Tia, the woman with the cake samples will be here shortly. Please don't be late. I've had an idea for the filling.'

James watched Julia Ferris glide gracefully across the hall and disappear through the drawing room door, and Tia shook her head.

'See what I mean?' she hissed. 'Anyone would think this is her wedding, not ours. Right, I suppose I'd better get ready.' She held up grubby fingers. 'I've been pricking out tomato plants in the greenhouse. Can't eat cake with dirty fingers.'

Personally, James couldn't see what the problem was. A spot of dirt never hurt anyone. It was good for the immune system, in fact. That was the problem – society, as a whole, was too clean, too sterile; there wasn't enough exposure to germs and—

'Are you going to stand there all day, or are you going to join me for a coffee and a slice of that lemon drizzle I was talking about?' William wanted to know. 'I won't have any cake with you, though – I think I just might have had my fill of cake by the end of the afternoon…'

'Actually, I've got to run,' James said. 'I've got a meeting at the council offices in an hour, so I'll just grab a slice from the kitchen, if that's OK with you?'

'Of course it is,' William said, with another gentle thump on the arm. 'I'll give you a call later, yeah, and maybe we can go for a pint?'

James left his friend to his extensive and complex wedding preparations (cake testing? Who knew?), immensely thankful that he wasn't going through the same thing himself. The thought of all the pomp and ceremony, not to mention the expense, filled him with dread.

If he were ever to get married, and that was a fairly remote possibility considering the distinct lack of anything in the way of romance in his life, then he would want a quiet, low-key, unobtrusive wedding. Of course he realised that his bride, whoever she may be, might very well have different ideas about it, but the thought of all eyes on him as he stood in the church in front of a cast of hundreds made him feel quite nauseous.

Being the best man at William and Tia's wedding was going to be bad enough. He was already having palpitations just thinking about all the things that could go wrong, like losing the ring, or allowing William to do something completely ridiculous on his stag night, such as getting a silly tattoo. And he hadn't even thought about the best man's speech yet.

Actually, that was a lie. He'd done nothing *but* think about it since William had asked him, and it had brought him out in a cold sweat ever since. Which was ironic, considering he was perfectly happy to stand up in front of a roomful of people and give a presentation on the benefits of his Vestal Verges project (which was exactly what he was going to do at the council offices later today, to try to persuade councillors to agree to seeding all suitable verges with wildflowers). Yet the thought of giving a speech at his oldest friend's wedding gave him the heebie-jeebies.

Taking his cake with him to eat in the car on the way, James tried to focus on his imminent meeting.

The creation of vestal verges wasn't as high profile as the reintroduction of wolves into areas in which they hadn't been seen for decades, but in some people's eyes, it was just as controversial.

Ever since he'd got back, he'd been campaigning for seeding the miles and miles of roadside verges and round-abouts with wildflowers, only trimming them back in late October when most of the bees, butterflies and other insects were winding down for the winter.

Not only would it be beneficial to the rapidly dwin-dling insect population, but it would save the council time and money, too. He acknowledged there would be an initial cost in the form of the purchase of a few tonnes of seeds, but this would be offset by not having to send crews out every few weeks to mow them, with the associated cost of fuel, equipment and so on.

He was aware he'd face some opposition, mostly from the 'we've-always-done-it-like-that' crowd, who were chronically resistant to any kind of change, and he'd prob-ably get some opposition from the health and safety lot, who would insist that leaving verges to their own devices would be a danger beyond compare.

God help him when he tried to implement his next idea, James thought, which was to turf the tops of bus shel-ters. Other countries had done it, so his proposal wasn't too off-the-wall. He'd calculated the acreage available and the subsequent impact on wildlife throughout the county, and it was fairly considerable, even though this was a rural area and bus stops weren't exactly plentiful.

Wolves it mightn't be, but in his opinion, every little bit that could be done to increase habitats for wildlife was vital, and quite often it was the little things which had the greatest impact.

And James Preece was on a mission to make his neck of the woods as wildlife-friendly as possible.

Chapter 3

Edie was first in, as always. Although the shop was technically open from ten a.m., Mrs Carrington hardly ever made an appearance before eleven, unless she had a bride booked in for an early appointment. It was rare for anyone to pop in for a browse, although it had been known to happen despite Mrs Carrington's frown of disapproval (she tried to operate an appointment-only system), so Edie anticipated having the next hour to herself.

After she hung up the dress she'd brought with her from home, the one she'd been working on yesterday when Danny had asked her for a pet, she intended to make a nice cup of tea before she started unpacking the veils which had been delivered yesterday. They were mostly Spanish and Portuguese lace, and cost more than Edie earned in a week, even if she included the occasional payment per dress for alterations which she did at home.

As usual, she'd skipped breakfast, so she ate a couple of biscuits with her cup of tea and gazed around the shop.

To be fair to Mrs Carrington, she might be a miserly old so-and-so but she knew what a wedding shop should look like, and the feeling of timeless elegance and understated luxury hung in the air like the expensive perfume her boss insisted on spraying around the room several times a day. No wonder the shop wasn't making any money if Mrs Carrington (Edie never, ever called her Moira, and Mrs Carrington had never indicated that she should) threw potential profits away by spraying them liberally in the air.

Chanel No 5 wasn't the most economical of air fresheners, although it did smell lovely. If it was up to Edie, she'd have displayed vases of freshly cut flowers everywhere and not just the solitary bunch on the coffee table, and let the natural scents of roses and peonies fill the air. Much better than any artificial scent.

But it wasn't up to Edie. Edie had no say in the running of Moira's whatsoever, even if she had worked there for nearly seven years and was the only employee. She did as she was told, having long ago discovered the error of making any kind of suggestion to Mrs Carrington.

She spent the next hour sorting out those veils, then when Mrs C (Edie would never dream of calling her that to her face) arrived for the first of only two appointments of that day, she spent an hour with a client who wanted a hand-made specially designed gown for the price of one from a local department store. The bride, her mother and her sister left without paying a deposit, and without saying they'd return either.

That was another problem with Moira's, Edie thought, as she carefully put the selection of dresses back in their respective places – the shop was neither one thing nor the other, but something in between. It couldn't compete on prices with the chain stores, yet it wasn't quite exclusive enough to attract many of the higher paying customers, the ladies who didn't want a run-of-the-mill, off-the-shelf dress. And that was what Edie was particularly good at – designing dresses – despite the fact that she'd dropped out of college before she'd completed the course, although she did promise herself she'd return to education one day.

One day had become eight years already, and with the sheer pressure of work and looking after Danny it didn't look as though that would happen any time soon. Besides, she couldn't afford to give up a regular monthly salary. She found it hard enough to make ends meet as it was.

On occasion, she did allow herself to wallow in a small puddle of self-pity. She'd been barely eighteen when she'd discovered she was pregnant. It had been a shock, to say the least. Especially when her baby's father didn't want to know. It was at that point that Edie decided if he didn't want to be in his son's life, then she wanted nothing from him. She would manage just fine on her own.

It hadn't been fine, but she had managed, and now here they were, her and Danny, very happy, thank you very much; although, she did wonder whether Danny felt the lack of a male role model in his life. Her mother had been a single parent, too, so it wasn't as though he had a maternal grandfather to fill part of that void.

Maybe that was the reason for him acting up a little recently – did he feel that he had to be the man of the house because there wasn't anyone else to fulfil the role?

It might explain—

'Edie! Kindly see if the ladies would like tea or coffee.' Mrs C's sharp tone broke her out of her reverie, and she hurried to see what the customers wanted.

She recognised one of them, Stevie, who owned Peggy's Tea Shoppe in the high street, and felt as though it would be a bit like taking coals to Newcastle to offer her refreshments. However, she did as she was told, and very soon she'd placed a pot of tea and a couple of delicate cups and saucers on the low table in front of the off-white plush sofa.

'Can you bring another cup, please?' Stevie asked. 'We're expecting another bridesmaid soon.'

Edie obliged and left the ladies discussing tiaras while she darted back into the business end of the shop. The front part was tiny, but the building was a three-storey one and quite generous. The ground floor contained the seating area where brides showed off the various dresses they tried on to their friends and family. Beyond that was the fitting room itself, and an area to store a few dozen dresses. Further back again was Mrs C's office and a small kitchen.

The first floor was where the majority of dresses were housed, and all the other things a bride simply couldn't do without, from hoops to go underneath the skirts to satin shoes which could be dyed any conceivable colour.

But Edie's domain was on the very top floor. That was where the magic happened, where she transformed a vague drawing on a piece of paper into a dress fit for Cinderella. Of course, it involved a considerable amount of work to get from the one to the other. During those many stages, Edie took as much home with her as she could, to work on when Danny had gone to bed, but most of it took place in her little eyrie. She had been tempted to Sellotape a sign on the door, saying 'Edie's Eyrie', but she'd never bothered, knowing Mrs C wouldn't see the humour in it and would make her take it down.

She heard Mrs Carrington call from the viewing area (as her boss grandly called it), 'Edie, bring out the Buckingham dress in ivory and nude.'

The Buckingham dress was one of Edie's creations (Mrs C insisted on calling each design by the name of a grand house) and she had made a couple of different sizes for trying-on purposes, plus three colour combinations. If the bride wanted one for herself, then Edie would make it from scratch, to measure, so each and every dress would perfectly fit the bride who wore it.

She'd already taken a rough guess at Stevie's size and she dashed upstairs to fetch the one she thought might fit, smiling to herself, when she heard Mrs C say, 'Excuse me, but I don't allow photos. These are all one-off designs. I can't have them copied. I'd be grateful if you'd put your phone away.'

In this instance, Edie agreed with her boss. She put her heart and soul into her gowns, and she'd be devastated if her designs were stolen and copied.

'Bring it here, girl,' Mrs Carrington ordered, as Edie stepped forwards, holding the dress as high as she could to show off the fall and flow of the fabric. She wished Mrs C would stop calling her 'girl' – it made her feel like a servant, not an employee.

'It's got an off-the-shoulder neckline and a fit-and-flare skirt,' Mrs Carrington said to the bride. 'Can you see how the nude silk underneath the lace complements the champagne colour of the bridesmaid's dress I've just shown you? You've got the figure to carry this off.'

Stevie most certainly did, Edie acknowledged. Stick-thin and straight-up-and-down figures didn't suit a dress like this. She'd created it with curves in mind, a celebration of womanhood. And Mrs C was right – the ivory and nude would show off Stevie's hair and skin tone to perfection.

Edie honestly didn't know how Mrs Carrington did it.

Not only did she insist on a consultation before the appointment proper, but she didn't allow any bride to view her stock. Never. There was a strict no-browsing policy in Moira's Wedding Shop, no rifling through rails of dresses, no fingers trailing over fabric. No half-pulling a gown away from the rail to take a closer look. What Mrs Carrington did was to consider everything her client had told her, then have Edie bring out a dress. *A* dress; just the one.

Nine times out of ten, the bride never asked to see another. Even if they were sceptical about trying it on, when they saw how wonderfully fabulous they looked in it, the idea of asking to see another wedding gown didn't even enter their heads.

Mrs C was also right when it came to the bridesmaids' dresses for this wedding. The champagne was perfect for both girls.

Hang on, wasn't that…?

The latecomer was Leanne Green, who'd been in the year above her in school. She hadn't seen her for ages, despite the fact that Leanne owned the flower shop around the corner. Hadn't she heard a rumour somewhere that Leanne was going to be in a floristry competition on TV?

'It's wonderful.' Stevie's face had lit up at the sight of the dress, and Leanne reached for a handily placed box of tissues on the coffee table and handed it to her friend.

'Try it on,' the other bridesmaid urged. 'I bet it'll look gorgeous.'

I bet it will, too, Edie thought. There was always some-thing of the fairy tale about the trying-on bit, as though the dress had the power to transform the most ordinary of women into a princess.

Mrs C made shooing motions with her fingers. 'Edie, take Miss Taylor into the fitting room. I'll be in shortly.'

'Edie? Edie Adams? Is that you?' Leanne had recognised her. 'Don't I know you from school?'

'You were in the year above me,' Edie said. She shot a wary glance at her boss. Mrs C hated her making small talk with her customers.

'I thought so. How are you?' Leanne gave her a wide smile and Edie smiled back. She'd never really known Leanne, but she'd seemed nice enough.

'Great, thanks,' she said. 'Excuse me, but I need to get Miss Taylor undressed.'

'Call me Stevie,' Stevie said. 'Everyone does.'

'Not everyone, Miss Taylor,' Mrs Carrington said. 'Now, if you don't mind, I have another bride in an hour…?'

'Sorry,' Leanne mouthed at Edie, and Edie turned away, biting back a smile.

Mrs C didn't have another bride in an hour. She didn't have another bride until tomorrow, but Edie supposed it wasn't good business to advertise the fact that she had all the time in the world. It was sad but true that if people perceived something to be in demand, then they wanted it too. At least, that's what Edie suspected Mrs Carrington thought, by the way she tried to create an air of exclusivity around the shop.

It took both Edie and Mrs Carrington to help Stevie into her dress (it was a very delicate operation) and when she was in it, it took Edie another fifteen minutes or so to adjust it. The sample, as it was called, could be clipped and pinned at various points, to simulate how the made-to-measure finished gown would appear. This one didn't look perfect on the bride (how could it, when it wasn't specifically made for her)? but it was enough to give Stevie and the other girls a hint of how beautiful she would look in it on the day.

Mrs C deliberately hadn't installed mirrors in the large changing room. Her argument was that she didn't want any bride of hers to see a halfway house – the bride was only allowed to gaze on the finished article, so with that in mind, Edie led her customer out into the viewing area and helped her onto the raised circular stand.

It always put a smile on her face when she saw a bride up there – it reminded her of a musical jewellery box she used to have as a child. When the lid was lifted, a ballerina popped up, turning on the spot. The stand in the viewing area turned too, so the bride's entourage could view the dress from all angles, and Edie often expected to hear the tinkling notes of *Swan Lake* as it did so.

'Oh. My. God.' Leanne clapped a hand to her mouth, her eyes wide. The other bridesmaid, who Edie didn't recognise, which was unusual for a small village such as Tanglewood, looked equally as stunned.

'Is that a good OMG, or a bad one?' Stevie asked, her expression worried.

Mrs Carrington stepped towards a white velvet curtain and took hold of a pull cord. 'Are you ready?'

Stevie nodded.

Mrs C opened the curtain.

When Stevie saw herself in the mirror, she cried.

So did Edie.

Lordy, but she loved her job!

Chapter 4

Edie hadn't been this excited in a long time. She'd been invited up to The Manor and she simply couldn't wait.

To be honest, it wasn't she who had been invited, it was Mrs Carrington, but Mrs C had informed her that Edie's presence was required on the consultation. It wasn't unusual for Edie to do this, although every other consultation which she'd sat in on had been in the shop, but what Julia Ferris wanted, Julia Ferris got.

Everyone in the village knew Lord and Lady Tonbridge. Not personally, obviously, but with The Manor having a ball every summer to which all the villagers were invited, there were very few people who could say they hadn't met one or the other of them. Lady Ferris made a point of shopping locally whenever she could, too, so she was a frequent sight on the high street. Until recently she'd never had any occasion to visit the little wedding shop in the courtyard, but with her only son getting married shortly, she now had a vested interest in all things bridal. Her daughter, Melissa, had got engaged last summer, but so far there'd been no mention of any date for the nuptials, so Julia Ferris's focus was firmly on those of her son. Rumour also had it that she was being a bit bridezilla about it, even though she wasn't the bride.

Edie hadn't been to The Manor before, despite the summer balls. They were grown-up affairs and she'd never been happy leaving Danny with her mother to go out partying half the night. Not with the state of her mother's health. Pauline wasn't a well woman and she already did her fair share of looking after Danny during the school holidays. Edie couldn't expect her to babysit him in the evening too.

Her first proper sight of the manor house and its extensive grounds took Edie's breath away. Set on one of the hillsides above the village, the views over the valley as the car wound its way up the sweeping drive were breathtaking. But Edie only gave the vista a passing glance, her attention riveted on the building itself. It looked even larger up close than it did from the road, and she could see why the Ferris family thought it would make a wonderful setting for a wedding. Apparently, William Ferris's marriage to Tia Saunders was intended to advertise the venue, and Julia wanted everything to be perfect.

Edie could envisage a bride standing on the wide, shallow steps leading to the impressive front doors, having photos taken with a marble column either side to frame her, and she was desperate to see the rest of the house. It was a perfect place for a wedding, she thought, from what she could see so far.

They were shown into a hallway with a sweeping staircase (there seemed to be a lot of sweeping going on, she thought), a massive chandelier dangling above it, glittering and sparkling in the sunlight streaming in from a glass window set high above in the domed ceiling. Dark and gloomy paintings of what Edie assumed were assorted staid and stern-looking ancestors adorned the walls, and she felt their eyes staring at her as they were escorted into the drawing room, where a tray with tea and coffee was already laid out.

Lady Tonbridge and the bride were waiting, and Lady Tonbridge rose to greet them. 'Do you wish me to send someone out to bring in the samples?' she asked.

Mrs Carrington smiled politely. 'No samples today. This is a consultation only. I'll return with what I consider to be suitable gowns when I know a little more about Miss Saunders's requirements.'

Lady Tonbridge blinked. 'Oh. I see. I assumed Tia would try a few things on.'

'Too early in the process,' Mrs C said. 'First, we need to determine what style will suit her best, and any preferences she might have.'

Edie listened to the conversation, but her attention was on Tia Saunders, whose expression was blank. But there were two spots of colour on her cheeks and her eyes flashed; Edie guessed the bride wasn't too happy being spoken about as though she wasn't in the room.

Once they were seated, with cups balanced on their knees (Edie trying valiantly to keep hers still and stop it from rattling in its saucer), Mrs C got down to business.

'Can you walk at all, Miss Saunders?' was her first question.

Edie froze, her cup halfway to her mouth, and Lady Tonbridge let out a tiny gasp.

Miss Saunders didn't seem at all bothered by the question. 'No,' she replied mildly.

'In that case, the focus will be on the bodice,' Mrs C said. 'It'll be all about the top half of the dress, and not so much the skirt. The last thing you want is for yards of material to get caught up in those wheels. You'll not be bothered about the back, either,' she added. 'Edie, are you making a note of all this?'

Edie nodded, putting her cup and saucer back on the table, and searching around in her bag for her pad. It wasn't like her to be so unprepared, but the magnificence of the old building and the presence of Lady Tonbridge had awed her somewhat.

'I'm thinking charmeuse. What do you think, Edie?' Mrs C fired at her, once Edie's pen was poised over the paper.

'Too plain. The fabric doesn't lend itself to too much decoration,' she said, without thinking.

Mrs Carrington narrowed her eyes at her. 'Yes, that's the point. Simple, elegant, understated. I think that's what you said you wanted?' She looked at Lady Tonbridge.

'What's charmeuse?' Miss Saunders asked.

'It's a lightweight fabric, with a shine to it similar to satin, but softer and not as stiff,' Edie explained, and Mrs C shot her a look, which Edie interpreted to mean that she should shut up.

She bowed her head and focused on the blank sheet of paper instead.

'It'll be perfect for you,' Mrs C insisted. 'And I think ivory, not white.'

'No, I think we'll go with white,' Lady Tonbridge said.

Was it her imagination, or had Miss Saunders's eyes flashed for a second? Was the bride not going to have any say in her dress at all?

Mrs C bowed her head. 'Certainly, white it is. Tell me, do you prefer off-the-shoulder, one-shoulder, sleeves…?'

'We were thinking of a crossover bustline with wide straps, weren't we, dear?' Lady Tonbridge said. 'Or maybe something draped, from here to here.' She demonstrated what she meant with her hands. 'Off-the-shoulder is a little vulgar, in my opinion.'

Miss Saunders said nothing, but Edie had the impression she'd like to say a great deal indeed.

'I'll bring a selection with me for our next appointment, and some fabric swatches,' Mrs C said. 'Once we decide on the style and fabric, we can then agree on any adornments or embellishments.'

'Super!' Lady Tonbridge exclaimed.

Miss Saunders didn't appear to think it was super at all. In fact, Edie could have sworn she was glowering underneath her apparently calm exterior.

'I trust it's OK for Edie to measure Miss Saunders?' Mrs Carrington asked Lady Tonbridge.

'Miss Saunders says that's fine,' the girl in the wheelchair said, tartly. 'I can speak for myself, you know,' she said to the woman who was soon to be her mother-in-law.

'Of course, dear, I was only trying to help.' Julia smiled brightly.

It was only Edie who caught Tia Saunders's muttered, 'Definitely trying,' as she approached the girl with her tape measure, pencil and pad in hand.

While she worked, Edie listened to the two matriarchs' conversation.

'Rest assured, the dress will be made-to-measure, and not an off-the-peg gown which has been altered,' Mrs C was telling the lady of the manor.

Edie glanced up in time to catch Lady Tonbridge's expression.

'Actually, with such a simple design, if you do have a pre-made dress in stock which could be altered, that might be a possibility.'

Mrs C raised an eyebrow. 'Hmm,' she said, tapping her fingers against her cheek. 'I'm sure I can find *something* suitable, but it won't be nearly as perfect as having a gown specially designed.'

Edie had heard talk that The Manor, along with many other grand old houses, was having to diversify to make ends meet, which explained opening the house up as a wedding venue. She'd also heard that Lord Tonbridge was running courses in things like coppicing and basket-weaving.

'Of course, whatever you think is best,' Lady Tonbridge said.

'My assistant, Edie, designs all my special-order dresses. You won't be disappointed.'

Edie begged to differ. From what she had seen and heard so far, she predicted that the bride would be very disappointed indeed. Understated and elegant was one thing, but Edie got the impression that Miss Saunders's tastes ran in an entirely different direction.

She'd just finished jotting down the bride's final measurement when the clatter of feet in the marble-tiled hallway caught her attention. The drawing room door burst open, and a man who she recognised as William Ferris strode in, closely followed by another man who Edie didn't know.

She straightened up and took a step back, not wanting to intrude on the family moment, but unable to escape.

'William!' Lady Tonbridge admonished. 'You could have knocked. Tia and I have been discussing wedding dresses. You know it's bad luck for the groom to see the dress before the big day.'

'What dress?' William Ferris glanced around the room, before heading for the untouched plate of biscuits on the table. 'Pink wafers!' he exclaimed. 'I haven't had these since you freed me from boarding school.'

'Don't be silly. You loved every minute of it. Where are my manners – let me introduce you. William, this is Mrs Carrington, who'll be designing Tia's wedding dress. Mrs Carrington, as you've probably guessed, this is my son, William, who is the groom, and his best man, James.'

A flurry of 'hello's and 'pleased to meet you's followed as Edie looked on, feeling somewhat awkward and a bit like one of the antique pieces of furniture which were dotted around the room.

'And this,' Miss Saunders said, 'is Edie, who I believe is the person who will actually be doing the designing. Have I got that right, Mrs Carrington?'

Heat flooded into Edie's cheeks as everyone stared at her, and she wished she really was part of the fixtures and fittings.

'You have. Edie Adams is my designer,' Mrs C announced, grandly, although Edie could tell from the tiny tic under her employer's left eye that Mrs Carrington wasn't in the least bit happy to be contradicted in front of Lady Tonbridge.

She kept her gaze on the floor, only looking up once the attention had moved on from her. But, to her consternation, she found William's best man studying her, and she blushed even more.

'So, have you decided on a dress, my darling?' Mr Ferris asked his fiancée, as he stuffed another pink wafer in his mouth. 'You ought to have one of these, James; they'll remind you of school.'

'Ugh, no thanks,' James said with an exaggerated shudder. 'I don't want to remember if I can help it.'

Miss Saunders took a deep breath. 'Yes, I have decided,' she said to the man standing beside her, but it was Edie who she was looking at.

'Good,' Lady Tonbridge said. 'I'll get Belinda to see you out. Shall we say, same time on Thursday?'

Without waiting for a reply, Lady Tonbridge picked up a small brass bell and tinkled it.

Crikey, Edie thought; this is just like being in an episode of *Downton Abbey*. She fully expected a maid to walk in, dressed in black and wearing a snowy white apron with a cap on her head. After such an image, Belinda, in a perfectly normal pleated skirt and a blouse, was a bit of a disappointment.

'Get started on it,' Mrs Carrington snapped, as Edie scuttled around to the passenger door and climbed in. 'I want something to show her ladyship by Thursday. I expect a mood board and a mock-up.'

'Of course,' Edie said. It didn't give her much time, but she could prepare a mood board after Danny had gone to bed this evening, and she had a basic mock-up she could adapt to Miss Saunders's measurements.

She did, however, get the feeling that Miss Saunders wasn't going to lie down and let her future mother-in-law walk all over her. Tia Saunders had something up her sleeve…

Chapter 5

James hesitated in the drawing room doorway. It wasn't the sight of Julia or Tia, and neither was it the older woman who had caused him to falter. It was the younger woman who was standing by Tia that gave him pause, and not just because of her delicate features and her long, wheat-blonde hair. It was her attitude that intrigued him – she reminded him of a fawn, all long-limbed and wary, giving him the impression that she would dart away at any second. A forest creature, with the light from the windows playing across her face and her grey eyes filled with caution, she seemed too fey for the staid respectability of Julia Ferris's very proper drawing room. Hell, it made him feel uncomfortable, too, and he was used to these kinds of surroundings.

Used to, but not *part of*. He was as out of place here as he suspected this girl felt.

He followed William further into the room as Julia exclaimed, 'William! You could have knocked. Tia and I have been discussing wedding dresses. You know it's bad luck for the groom to see the dress before the big day.'

William was more interested in a plate of biscuits and tucked into one as his mother made the introductions.

Was this girl also here to talk about dresses? James wondered, as Julia introduced them. He did notice, though, that she didn't introduce the girl, and neither did the woman who was with her, Mrs Carrington.

Was he missing something? Was there a subtext he wasn't aware of? Why was she being ignored?

He was about to walk up to her and introduce himself (because Julia clearly wasn't going to do it – if she hoped to make a success of this business venture of hers, then she needed to learn some manners), but before he could move, Tia spoke.

'And this,' she said, 'is Edie, who I believe is the person who will actually be doing the designing. Have I got that right, Mrs Carrington?'

The girl blushed, pinking her cheeks. She looked even more awkward and uncomfortable than she'd done before, and his heart went out to her.

'You have. Edie Adams is my designer,' Mrs Carrington said, but there was an edge to her voice that James didn't like. He was under the impression that she wanted Julia to believe that she designed the dresses herself, and he wondered if Tia had unwittingly landed the girl in it. He hoped not; Edie (what a lovely, sweet, old-fashioned name) seemed far too timid and shy to be able to deal with any comeback from her employer.

Still, he reasoned, she must know what she was doing.

He was still studying her when she looked up and found him staring, and her blush deepened until she was positively glowing. Radiant was the word that came to mind…

'So, have you decided on a dress, my darling?' William was busy with the pink wafers. 'You ought to have one of these, James; they'll remind you of school.'

33

'Ugh, no thanks. I don't want to remember if I can help it.' School, although not unpleasant per se, wasn't a period of his life he was particularly fond of, especially since he was the poor boy who had only attended private school because of a bursary. No one was supposed to know about it, but all the other boys did – they only had to ask where he lived for them to make an educated guess.

'Yes, I have decided,' Tia said, and something in her voice made him look at her; he was pretty certain it wasn't William she was speaking to, but Edie.

'Good,' Julia said, before turning to Mrs Carrington, and saying, 'I'll get Belinda to see you out. Shall we say, same time on Thursday?' Then she rang that silly little bell of hers.

James was used to her odd ways, but he had to hide a smile at the incredulous expression on Edie's face. Trying not to make it obvious that he was watching her as she followed her employer to the door, he turned away, to notice that Tia was trying to catch his attention.

Opening his mouth to ask her what she wanted, he shut it again when she widened her eyes and gave a little shake of her head, then glanced meaningfully at Julia.

'I'll just pop along to the kitchen,' he said. 'See if there's any cake left.'

'Ask Chef to rustle you up some lunch,' Julia offered. 'You boys must be starving. William, I think your father wanted to see you about the progress on the workshops.'

'While he's doing that, I'll have a quick word with Chef,' Tia said.

'Whatever for?' Julia wanted to know.

'I said I'd go through the sample menus with him. He's working on the costings.'

34

Julia shrugged and waved Tia away.

James fell into step behind her. 'Did you want me for something?' he asked.

'Shhh! That woman's got ears like a bat. Let's go outside.' She led the way past the kitchen and out through what used to be the servants' entrance. James had the feeling it still was, because her ladyship encouraged everyone to use it. It was only William who insisted on going in and out through the front door, and he did that solely to annoy his mother.

'Got to get one's little pleasures where one can,' his friend had told him once, 'and irritating my mother when she's being silly is one of them.'

'What do you need my help with?' James asked her when Tia drew to a halt.

They were halfway across the courtyard, but still she looked over her shoulder to check they couldn't be overheard.

'I'm going to make an appointment with the designer, Edie, and I want you to take me,' she said.

'Can't you go yourself?' he asked. 'I mean, I don't mind driving you, but you're perfectly capable of driving your-self, aren't you?' He hoped there was nothing wrong with her that meant she was no longer able to drive. William had told him it had taken her ages to get behind the wheel of her modified car, but once she'd found the courage, she'd relished the freedom it gave her.

'Of course I can,' she scoffed, 'but I don't want Julia or William to know what I'm doing, so I'm going to have to use you as a go-between.'

'It's all very cloak and dagger. Are you planning on murdering someone? A certain future mother-in-law, perhaps?'

'Don't tempt me.' Tia's tone was grim. 'You saw how she was in there.' She jerked her head at the house. 'It was even worse before you arrived. She's only gone and decided what dress I'm going to wear.'

'For what?'

'My wedding, you goose.'

'Oh...'

'Exactly! I've let her get away with a lot because I know she's using our wedding to showcase The Manor, and I fully understand and support that. Mostly. But I'm drawing the line at her interfering with the dress.'

'The Dress,' he repeated, giving it a suitable degree of importance.

'I'm going to sort out my own wedding dress, thank you, and you and Edie are going to help me do it.'

He narrowed his eyes. 'Does Edie know?'

'Not yet, but she soon will.'

'Why all this cloak-and-dagger stuff? Why not tell Julia how you feel?'

'Because she won't let it lie. You know what she's like – she won't be able to help herself. If anyone checked in the dictionary, under "interfering" it would say, "see Lady Tonbridge". Besides, I want my dress to be a total surprise; I don't want every man and his dog to have seen it before my big day. If I thought Moira Carrington would support me, I'd go straight to her, but she's made it clear whose side she's on.'

'Are there sides?'

'There are,' Tia replied, firmly. 'And I want Edie Adams on mine. Now, will you help me or not?'

James blew out his cheeks. He really shouldn't get involved, but if it meant he had a chance to see Edie again, he'd take it. 'OK,' he said, 'I'm in. What do you need me to do?'

Chapter 6

Mrs Carrington usually closed the shop at four p.m. every day, unless a consultation or appointment had been booked in. There was little in the way of passing trade to stay open for, because virtually all Moira's clients came to her via word of mouth. Edie did think (and had suggested) that Mrs C should do some advertising, even if it was just a simple board on the high street, by the entrance to the courtyard, but she was having none of it. How she stayed in business, Edie had no idea.

Four o'clock suited Edie just fine. School officially finished at three thirty, but on three days out of five, Danny remained behind at various clubs until four, so she was able to fetch him herself. On the other two, her mother usually collected him, and he spent the day with his granny on Saturday, too. The arrangement suited everyone, although having him all day on Saturday was getting to be a bit much for her mum these days. She'd never been particularly well, having been diagnosed with fibromyalgia, but lately she was struggling more than usual, and Edie wished she was able to drop down to a half-day on Saturdays, even though the decrease in her wages would hurt.

The other issue Edie had was not having enough time to work on her own designs, because she was so busy with the demands Moira made on her. Ever since she could remember, she'd been interested in fashion. Not the everyday sort, but the special occasion sort. She blamed Barbie and the selection of princess ballgowns she'd been given for Christmas one year.

The clothes that women wore to work or to take the kids to the park held no interest for her – what they might wear to a ball, or a prom, or on their wedding day, did. She loved the fabrics, the flow and fall of them; she loved the decorations, the cut, the drape, the way the dresses made people feel when they wore them – like princesses.

It was such a shame that she'd never felt like that herself. She'd never tried on anything she'd designed or made, and she never would, unless she'd designed it for herself to wear on her own special occasion.

Tell a lie, she did make her own simple everyday dresses, the occasional skirt and the even more occasional playsuit, because that's how she'd honed her skills as a dressmaker, making clothes for herself. She remembered begging her mum to take her to a charity shop so she could pick out a dress to alter. And when her grandmother had given her an old Singer sewing machine and shown her how to use it, Edie had been in her element. Over the years, she'd become quite skilled indeed.

Mrs C had already left for the day and Edie was making sure the viewing room was pristine before she finished, when she heard the shop door open with a discrete tinkle.

Who on earth could that be, she wondered, hoping it wasn't a drop-in. She hated not being able to let excited brides wander freely among the dresses, to finger the delicate fabric and admire the lace and beading. Some people wanted to browse first, to get an idea of what they might like; not every bride wanted to be issued with a fait accompli, despite Mrs C being right about her recommendations more often than not. Her employer's method seemed to suck the wonder and fun out of the whole process of choosing a wedding dress, Edie thought.

Duster in hand, she glanced over her shoulder, and her eyes met those of the man she'd seen yesterday in Lady Tonbridge's drawing room.

Her stomach did an odd flip, and for a second she felt decidedly strange, all fluttery and out of sorts, and briefly wondered if she'd forgotten to eat her lunch.

'Edie, isn't it?' he asked.

His voice was deeper than she remembered, but he still had the cultured tones of the British upper class. Not anywhere near as plummy as Julia Ferris or the Queen (Edie thought Lady Tonbridge actually out-queened Queen Elizabeth), but more like one of the younger royals, Prince William maybe.

'I'm sorry, but Mrs Carrington's not here,' she replied.

'I know; I waited until I saw her leave. Will she be long?'

'Er, she won't be back until tomorrow. Would you like to make an appointment?'

'With her?' He looked appalled. 'No thanks! She's scary.'

Edie allowed a small smile to play across her lips. Mrs C was certainly scary, all right, even when you got to know her – possibly more so, then.

'Um, is there anything I can help with?' she asked. It felt quite alien to have a male presence in what was predominantly a female preserve, although it wasn't unheard of. Most brides-to-be brought their mothers,

40

their sisters, their friends, or a mixture of all three, but there had been a few brides over the years who'd brought their father, brother, or a male friend. A man did seem out of place, though, and Edie got the impression that most of them were glad to escape, shooting out of the door with alacrity and deep breaths.

'Tia sent me,' he said.

'Tia?'

'Miss Saunders.'

'Oh. Is there anything wrong?'

'That depends on your point of view. Tia wants to decide on her own wedding dress, and she wants you to make it for her. But it has to be done in secret.'

Edie blinked. 'Excuse me?'

'Tia wasn't at all happy with the way things went yesterday. She feels that Julia and scary-lady ran roughshod over her.'

'Scary-lady…?'

'Your Mrs Carrington.'

Edie twisted her lips and tried to keep her laugh in.

'I mean, I don't blame Tia for wanting to do this on the sly,' he was saying. 'I would too. The pair of them made quite a formidable team, and I only caught the tail end of it. Don't get me wrong, Tia is a feisty girl and she's more than capable of standing up for herself, but what's the point in having to suffer months of argy-bargy when she can fly under the radar and appear in the dress of her choice at the last minute when it's too late for anyone to do anything about it?'

'Why, indeed,' Edie murmured. Tia Saunders had her sympathy, but it wouldn't be as easy as James was making it sound. For one thing, it would be more than her job was worth to go behind Mrs C's back. For another, the logistics would mean she'd almost certainly be caught out.

'Will you help her?' he asked.

'Why doesn't she just go to another wedding shop? There's a decent one in Abergavenny and a couple in Hereford.'

James shrugged. 'No idea. But she's asked me to ask you, so that's what I'm doing.'

'I don't think so,' she began. 'Not because I don't want to, but it'll cause ructions all round if Mrs Carrington finds out. I don't want to lose my job.'

'It wouldn't come to that, would it?'

'It might.' It probably would, although Mrs C would struggle to replace her – not because she was the only dressmaker around, but because no one else would be prepared to work such long hours for so little pay, for a boss who thought so little of her. So, if that was the case, maybe she could take the risk after all…?

Edie gave herself a mental shake. What on earth was she thinking to even consider it?

'Is that your final answer?' James asked.

Edie nodded slowly, reluctantly. She hated turning down work, but she had no choice. There was no way Mrs Carrington would turn a blind eye to Edie being in direct competition with her. And Edie didn't blame her – the woman had a business to run, after all.

'Pity. Tia definitely didn't want white, but it looks like that's what she's going to get,' he said.

He sounded genuinely sorry for Miss Saunders. Edie was, too. No bride should be forced to wear something they neither liked nor wanted on their special day.

'What colour was she thinking of?' Edie asked, intrigued. First-time, younger brides nearly always went for white, off-white, or ivory.

'She mentioned something about grey and silver, but I could have got that wrong. Wedding dresses aren't exactly my forte,' he said.

Edie wondered what his forte was, and a little tremor shot through her. This man, with his touching concern and desire to help out his best friend's fiancée, was far too handsome for his own good. She'd discovered in the past that handsome is as handsome does: her grandmother's expression, not hers. When she'd first heard it, she'd had no idea what it had meant. Post-Danny, she did. His father had been wickedly good looking, and look where that had got her. She didn't trust this man further than she could throw him – this time she'd borrowed the expression from her mother – no matter how nice and genuine he seemed.

Why was she having these thoughts, anyway, she wondered. It wasn't as though he'd come here to see *her*. He'd come here because Tia Saunders had asked him to. Edie's reaction to him was her problem and nothing to do with him. It wasn't his fault that something about him made her tummy flip-flop.

There, it did it again, and all because he was gazing at her with such a pleading and hopeful expression in those hazel eyes of his. He reminded her of Josh Duhamel in the film *Safe Haven* (which just happened to be one of her favourite films of all time) except younger, and with lighter hair. And better looking.

For goodness' sake, she said to herself, this has got to stop. She had more important things to think about than a man. Like, how was she going to keep this madcap project from Mrs C, for instance? Not that she had any intention of accepting the commission, of course; but if she did…

'Silver and grey?' Edie envisaged Tia Saunders in a dress with a scooped neckline, the bodice tight-fitting to her waist, the skirt flowing gently to her ankles, draping down over her legs in a cascade of silk georgette.

She risked another glance at James, her attention momentarily caught by the breadth of his shoulders and muscles beneath his T-shirt, and she wondered if he worked out or whether he'd come by his physique by doing something like rowing or playing rugby. Didn't many privately educated boys do those kinds of sports? And if he was such good friends with William Ferris, Edie guessed that they probably went to the same school or university. It had been Monmouth School for Boys and then Oxford for William. She'd bet it would have been roughly the same for James. They certainly had the same upper-class accent and the same air of confidence.

'I thought wedding dresses were supposed to be white, like it was the law or something,' he said, with a smile to show he was joking. 'Personally, I think white is a bit boring.'

Edie raised her eyebrows. 'What colour would you like your fiancée to wear?'

'It's a bit of a moot point, considering I haven't got one and I don't have a girlfriend either, but if I did, I'd want her to wear whatever she wanted.'

'Ooh, good answer.' Was she flirting with him? It certainly felt like it from her end. But it *was* a good answer, very diplomatic and tactful.

His smile broadened into a grin. 'I thought so, too,' he said, 'which is why it would be fantastic if you could help Tia wear what she wants on her wedding day.'

Edie shook her head. 'That's not fair.'

'No, it's not.'

'Do you always get your own way?'

'Does that mean you'll do it?'

'I'll think about it.'

He nodded once, a slight dip of his head. 'You've got her number.'

Edie paused. 'Actually, I haven't. There's a landline number for The Manor in the book, but not one for Miss Saunders.'

'Call her Tia, please. She'll want you to.'

'But Mrs Carring—'

'—isn't here,' he finished for her. 'And if the pair of you are going to be sneaking around like a couple of girls bunking off school, then I don't think you need to stand on ceremony, do you?'

Edie supposed not. A thought occurred to her. 'What about the dress Lady Tonbridge has ordered?'

James shrugged. 'Make it anyway.'

'But that means Tia will be paying for two dresses.'

'She knows, but she doesn't care. I mean, she *does* care, but Nick, her brother, has offered to help with the cost, because he knows how much this means to her. Ever since the accident that put her in the wheelchair, Tia has been worried about losing control of her life, and for a while she did. But William's told me that she's finally got her mojo back, and I'd hate to see anything change that.'

'Blackmail,' Edie said, accusingly. 'Emotional blackmail.'

45

He chuckled. 'If it works… Anyway, think about it and give her a call.' He took his phone out of his pocket and said, 'Give me your number and I'll send Tia's mobile number across to you.'

Hesitantly, because she still wasn't convinced about the whole thing despite his sweet talk, Edie fetched her phone.

'OK, you've got my number too,' he said, when they were done. 'By the way, I don't think we were properly introduced. My name's James Preece, and whether you design a dress for Tia or not, I'm delighted to meet you.'

He held out his hand, and Edie took it.

A bolt of *something* shot between them, and she drew in a sharp breath. Had he felt it, too?

'Don't be worried, Edie. If you say yes, I'll do everything in my power to make sure your dragon of a boss doesn't find out.'

He held her hand for a moment longer, then let go. Her whole hand tingled and she felt the lingering warmth of his skin on hers.

'Nice to meet you, too,' she said softly, as he slipped out of the shop and disappeared around the corner.

But that was the problem, wasn't it? It had been very nice to meet him indeed. Too nice.

She needed to rein in her attraction, because he was way out of her league. He moved in far more elevated circles than she ever could, and why would a man with his money and privilege look twice at a penniless single mother? He wouldn't. If she wasn't careful, she was in danger of developing a crush on him and might even have her heart bruised.

James Preece was simply being pleasant and polite. Any spark which she'd felt had been purely on her side and needed to be tamped down before it affected her judgement.

She'd have a good think about Tia Saunders and her wedding dress later tonight, but she resolved not to make a final decision until she'd spoken to the girl in question and found out exactly what Tia wanted her to make.

But all through Danny's tea and her late supper, when she was working at her table surrounded by scissors, pins and measuring tapes, all she could think about was grey georgette and James's hazel eyes.

Chapter 7

James came to collect Edie and take her to The Furlongs, Tia's brother's stables. It was two days since he'd spoken to her in Moira's, and she'd thought long and hard about what she intended to do.

He'd parked on the high street, but he'd no sooner knocked on her door than she had opened it, Danny crowding close behind her.

Edie stepped to the side. 'This is my son, Danny. I'm afraid he'll have to come with us.' She hated mixing her private life with business, but this evening she had no choice; her mother was under the weather and couldn't possibly look after him.

She watched James's reaction. Apart from a slight raise of an eyebrow, the news that she had a child didn't seem to faze him.

'Hi, Danny,' he said, and stuck out his hand. 'Pleased to meet you. I'm James.'

Danny glanced at her, and she nodded. She could tell her son was a little taken aback to be treated in such a grown-up manner but was delighted all the same.

'Are you my mum's boyfriend?' he asked.

Sudden heat warmed Edie's cheeks. 'Danny! I told you, this is work.'

'Jack's mum has a boyfriend, and he goes out with them sometimes,' Danny said.

She sent a widely-smirking James an apologetic look. 'Sorry,' she mouthed.

'That's OK. At least I know you're single.' His smile disappeared. 'Oh, darn it, I said that out loud, didn't I?'

It was her turn to smirk. 'You did.'

'I mean, I don't know if it's even true; you might well have a boyfriend but haven't introduced him to Danny yet.'

'I don't,' she replied, shortly. Since when did she have time for boyfriends? And even if she did, she'd certainly not be like Jack's mum and have a different guy every week. Neither would she let him meet her son; not until she was 100 per cent certain that the man in question was going to stick around. The last thing she needed was for Danny to get attached to some fella, and then for him to bugger off and leave the child heartbroken.

'So, do I bring him, or do you want to reschedule?' Edie asked. 'He'll be no trouble, but I fully understand if Miss Saunders – Tia – wants to make the appointment for another time.'

'I'm sure it'll be fine. There'll be plenty to keep him amused at the stables, I'm sure. I tell you what, I'll amuse Danny while you chat to Tia. How does that sound? Would you like to see some horses, Danny?'

Danny's eyes lit up. 'Can I, Mum? I'll be good, I promise.'

Edie had no doubts about her son's behaviour, but she didn't like leaving him in the care of someone she'd only just met and knew nothing about.

'We'll see,' she said, meaning no.

Danny wasn't fooled. 'She means "no",' he sighed.

'Maybe next time, eh? Or perhaps you can have a look at the horses when your mum's finished? She can have a look, too.'

Edie thought that was a much better suggestion. 'If Tia doesn't mind,' she said.

'I'm sure she won't,' he said, and she was conscious of his eyes on her as she grabbed a jacket each for her and Danny, then locked her front door. Fancy him wanting to know if she had a boyfriend. She should have said yes, but she wouldn't have said so in front of Danny. It would be too unsettling for him to think there was another man in her life, especially when there wasn't.

James headed in the same direction that Mrs Carrington had taken the other day, but turned off before they came to The Manor, and he steered the car up a winding, twisty lane until she saw a sign for The Furlongs.

Edie hadn't met Nick Saunders, Tia's brother (she didn't get out all that much), but she knew of him. The whole village did – he was their resident showjumping celebrity. He'd won medals in the Olympics and had been on the *Horse of the Year* show on TV. She'd heard he didn't compete a great deal himself any more, despite the fact that he wasn't much older than Tia. Instead he trained other riders and was also involved in The Manor in some capacity – she wasn't sure what, exactly, but she thought it was something to do with teaching disabled people to ride.

The Furlongs, she saw, consisted of a long, low bungalow, a large yard flanked by a couple of stable blocks, and several barn-type buildings. Everything was neat and clean, with no hint of the muck and grime she'd expected to see.

James parked his 4x4 and came around to her side to open the door and help her down. Danny had been bouncing with excitement in the back seat on the short journey, but now he was staring avidly out of the window.

'Horses!' he exclaimed, as he got out. 'See? Three of them.'

Sure enough, three inquisitive equine heads were poking over their stable doors, ears pricked forwards, large dark eyes limpid and curious.

'Would you like to say hello to them?' James offered.

'Maybe after I've spoken with Tia,' Edie said, keen to get the meeting out of the way before the reality of what she was doing sank in and she changed her mind. This could cost her her job.

James led the way to the house and knocked on the door before walking inside.

Edie and Danny hung back. She didn't like just walking into someone's house without being invited, but James seemed quite at home, so she followed him reluctantly.

Tia was waiting for them in the living room. She'd pulled her wheelchair up to a table which was scattered with papers and was poring over them. As Edie drew closer, she saw they were a mixture of typed notes, sketches and printed photos.

'Thank you for coming,' Tia said, looking up and offering her hand. 'I wasn't sure you would.'

'I'm still not sure,' Edie said, shaking it.

Tia guessed the reason immediately. 'No one needs to know, and I won't tell if you won't. James has very kindly volunteered to do the running around and act as a go-between, and the fittings can be done here, so there's no need to go near either The Manor or the shop.'

James snorted. 'Volunteered? Railroaded, is the correct term. She guilt-tripped me into it,' he explained to Edie.

Yeah, just like he'd done to her...

'And who's this?' Tia asked, looking at Danny, who was half-hiding behind his mum, overcome with shyness.

'My son, Danny. Sorry, I wouldn't normally bring him to meet a client...' Edie trailed off.

'No worries, this isn't exactly a normal situation.'

True. Edie had never been part of a clandestine wedding gown creation before. It would certainly make life interesting.

The old Chinese proverb of 'may you live in interesting times' came to mind, but she shoved it away. She'd made her decision and had no intention of going back on it, especially since she'd glimpsed the work Tia had already put into her dream dress.

'What did you have in mind?' Edie asked. 'James mentioned something about silver and grey?'

Tia's face lit up. 'I don't want white. I want something different, something memorable. All eyes are on the bride anyway, especially one in a wheelchair, so I want to stand out from the crowd. I don't do traditional. I want a dress that'll make people sit up and take notice.'

'Try red,' James suggested.

'Go away, James,' Tia said. 'You've done your part, now let the grown-ups talk.' Her wide smile showed she was teasing. 'Go and show Danny the Shetland ponies. If Edie's agreeable, he might even be able to have a little ride. There's no one in the manège, so you can use that.'

Edie shook her head. 'I don't want to put anyone out...' she began.

'Nonsense! It's me who's putting you out. I'm asking you to do me a huge favour, so let me do something nice for Danny. It's not much, but I'm sure he'll enjoy it.'

'He'll be safe enough with me,' James said. 'I promise. And if you don't want him to ride, he'll enjoy stroking noses. Both Shetlands are calm and quiet, especially if Danny gives them half an apple each. They'll be his friends for life.'

'Please, Mum, please. Can I? I've never stroked a horse before.'

Edie gave in. She would only be a short distance away, and for some inexplicable reason, she trusted James. 'OK, but be good, and do exactly as James tells you. Horses can be dangerous.'

'Come on, sprout,' James said to Danny. 'Let's go bother some ponies. Shetlands are ponies, not horses, and you'll see what I mean when you meet them...'

Edie listened to James prattling on as he took her son out of the living room, his voice fading slowly.

'Danny will be fine, you know,' Tia said. 'James, despite the looks and the attitude, is quite a responsible guy. A nice guy.'

Edie bit her lip. She was beginning to think that way, too. But the problem was, she didn't want to think about James Preece at all.

'Silver and grey?' she reminded Tia.

'Ah, yes. This is the sort of thing I have in mind.' She patted the chair next to her, indicating Edie should take a seat, and the two of them spent the next thirty minutes or so discussing design and fabric, until, when they were done, Edie had a clear view of what Tia's dress would look like.

A soft grey underskirt in a pale silk georgette would flow wonderfully under a sheer silver fabric. The bodice would be more structured, with a scoop neckline, and covered in pearls and diamante appliqué – the details of which had yet to be worked out, because first of all, Edie needed to source the fabric.

'I'll do a mock-up in polyester and chiffon first,' Edie explained, 'where all the kinks can be ironed out. It won't be perfectly stitched – I'll save that for the dress itself – but it'll give you a pretty good idea of what the completed gown will look like, and it's at this stage that we can play with the fit. You might decide you don't like where the waist sits, or that a different neckline will suit you better.'

'Won't that take an awful lot of time and effort?'

Edie smiled. 'That's what makes a hand-made gown so special. But no, I can run a sample dress up in an afternoon, and the fabric won't be wasted. It can be reused for other mock-ups, so the cost at this stage is minimal.'

'It's not the cost I'm worried about. It's the time. Will you be able to fit this in?'

'Yes. Definitely. The biggest time-suck will be finding the right fabric and sewing the beads on. Each one needs to be stitched on individually, otherwise if one catches and it's on the same length of thread as another, the whole lot will come off.'

'I see. What's the next step?'

'I'll come back with a value version of your dress, and I'll bring swatches of fabric for you to choose from, plus a selection of pearls, beads, appliqués and anything else I think will work. If you're happy with the basic design at that point, then we can discuss the decoration.' Edie hesitated, then said, 'If you want a veil, I can use the same fabric for it as the top layer of the skirt, and mirror some of the beading. Or if you want, I can show you a variety of pre-made ones.'

'I like your idea,' Tia said firmly. 'I'll be wearing my hair up in a chignon of some kind – I haven't totally decided yet – and a veil on top of that would look fantastic.'

Edie had all she needed for now, so after she'd gathered up her notes and put the borrowed sketches and photos in her bag, she was ready to go.

Her son, however, had other ideas.

He was still with James somewhere on the grounds, so Tia suggested they go and find him. 'He'll either be in the manège on the back of one of the long-suffering ponies, or James will be showing him the finer points of conservation, like field margins.'

Edie had no idea what Tia was talking about, and it must have shown on her face, because the girl let out a laugh. 'A manège is a type of indoor training area, and field margins are strips of land at the edges of fields that have been allocated to wildlife, meaning they're not culti-vated or grazed. The first thing James did when he came home was to bully Nick and Edgar Ferris into creating these field margins. He's busy trying to persuade other farmers in the area to do the same, and he can be quite insistent, in a nice sort of way, when he wants to be.'

'So I found out,' Edie muttered, then slightly louder, she asked, 'Is that what he does? Some kind of conserva-tion?'

Tia negotiated a small drainage channel in the yard and Edie wondered if she should help, before deciding against it, not wanting to interfere or to seem patronising. If Tia needed assistance, then Edie was sure Tia would ask for it.

'Here we are,' Tia announced, entering a wide door set into a barn wall.

Edie halted, amazed to see her son sitting on top of a small pony, a hard hat on his head, reins in his hands, looking for all the world as though he'd been riding for years.

She blinked back sudden tears. He looked so happy, so full of joy to be sitting astride the pony, and she was abruptly very aware that this was something else she wouldn't be able to afford for her son to do. Although she was thrilled that he'd had the experience, she knew it might be the first and last time he'd sit on a horse. Riding lessons were expensive, and even if she scraped the money together for another one, she'd never be able to take him – the nearest riding centre was miles away and she didn't have a car. Which was why James had been asked to pick her up and bring her to The Furlongs.

'He's played with kittens, stroked a couple of jumpers, then he decided he'd like to have a go on Pickles,' James told her.

Edie noted that although he was keeping his attention on Danny the whole time, James appeared relaxed, and some of the initial tension which had shot through her when she first saw her son on the pony's back seeped away.

Danny waited until he was in the car before he asked the question Edie knew he was itching to ask. 'Can I have a pony?'

'Erm, I don't think so, love; we haven't got anywhere to keep him.'

James shot her an amused glance which she caught out of the corner of her eye.

'She can live in the yard,' Danny suggested. 'You said we can't have a dog or a cat because they'd have to live indoors, but ponies live outside.' He sounded triumphant.

'Don't you think the yard is a bit too small for a pony?'

He considered her comment. 'No. Pickles is small. He'd fit. And I wouldn't have to walk him, like I'd have to walk a dog.'

'You'd have to ride him, though. You couldn't keep him cooped up the yard all the time. Besides, he'd have to walk through the house to get to it, and we can't have a horse traipsing through the house, can we?'

She could see James trying not to laugh, and a flash of annoyance went through her; she wished she hadn't agreed to let him show Danny around the stables. Now look what he'd done.

'Aw, Mum.' Danny's voice became a bit whiny, which surprised her, because he wasn't usually a whiny child. 'I bet James would let me have a pony.'

'I most certainly would not,' James said. 'Your mother is right; ponies are happy in big fields, not in small spaces.'

'The big horses were in stables,' Danny pointed out.

'Yes, but they only stay in there for a short time, like when they are being groomed or if they need their hooves checked. There wasn't a horse in every stable, was there?'

Reluctantly, Danny shook his head. 'No, but…'

'The rest of them are in the fields, where they have lots of grass to eat and other horses to play with. You wouldn't want the pony to be lonely, would you?'

'No, but I'd be its friend, so it wouldn't be lonely.'

'I'm sure you'd be a very good friend, but horses and ponies are herd animals, which means they like to be with others of their kind, and they get upset when they're not.'

Edie gave James a grateful little smile. At least he'd backed her up, and his arguments were sensible. She always tried to explain things properly to Danny, and not to resort to 'because I said so', although she sometimes found those very words popping out of her mouth on occasion when he'd driven her to distraction. Her son was a good kid, but that didn't mean he wasn't capable of playing her up now and again.

'Mum won't let me have a dog or a cat, either,' Danny announced.

She let out a sigh. 'We've been over this,' she said to him. 'I would if I could, but I can't.' She turned to James. 'My house is rented. No pets,' she explained, shortly.

The rest of the journey was undertaken in complete silence, and soon James drew the car to a halt in the high street, just outside the entrance to the courtyard.

'I'm sure it won't be long before I see you again,' James said as she and Danny got out.

Edie was sure it wouldn't be either, and she honestly didn't know how she felt about that.

Chapter 8

'Well?' Tia demanded.

James gave his friend's fiancée a questioning look, 'Well, what?'

'I saw the way you looked at Edie Adams.'

Unnerved, he made sure his expression was blank. 'I don't know what you mean.'

He did, though. He knew exactly what Tia was referring to, although he hadn't realised anyone else had noticed how smitten he was with the little seamstress. He wasn't very good at hiding his interest, but then, there hadn't been many women he'd felt such an instantaneous attraction to. In fact, she was the first to stir something strange, unidentifiable, though not entirely unwelcome in his chest.

Not that he'd been without girlfriends – far from it. He'd had his fair share, but they'd all been short-lived affairs and he'd never felt too concerned when they'd ended. He'd not felt all that concerned when they'd begun either, if he was honest. He'd tended to fall into relationships which were more based on circumstances than a genuine connection. Take the girl he'd met when he was at Yellowstone National Park, for instance – she was as driven and as passionate about conservation as he was, and they'd worked together closely for several months; it had been almost inevitable that a relationship had followed. But when she'd moved on to do research in Finland, he certainly wasn't heartbroken, and the whole thing had ended in cheerful friendliness and a vague promise to keep in touch.

The very nature of his job, up until now, had also meant it was hard to keep a relationship going; he'd moved around too much, for one thing, and for another, his heart and his head had been claimed by his job, and there hadn't been room in his life for anything else.

Until he'd returned home.

Until he'd met Edie Adams.

He guessed she was roughly the same age as him, possibly a year or two younger, which meant she must have been quite young when she had Danny.

Nice kid, he thought; well-mannered, thoughtful, eager to learn. She'd done a good job with him.

He wondered who the father was, and whether he was still on the scene.

Not that it mattered if he was, because she didn't appear to be in a relationship now.

What she did appear to be was wary, but whether it was of him as a person or men in general, he couldn't tell. She'd been pleasant enough and friendly; however, he didn't get the impression she was attracted to him, although he could have sworn there had been a brief spark when they'd shaken hands – but perhaps that had been his imagination. Or wishful thinking.

Tia was scrutinising him, he realised. And she had a knowing look on her face, as if she could tell what he was thinking.

'Don't be coy,' she said. 'I saw it the first time you met her. You couldn't take your eyes off her.'

'I felt annoyed for her,' he said. 'What with Julia and her own employer ignoring her like that. It wasn't right. I'm glad you stepped in.'

'You expect me to believe that?'

He shrugged. Tia could believe what she liked.

'Why don't you ask her out?'

'Why don't you mind your own business?'

Tia chuckled, and he realised he'd played it all wrong. Instead of going along with it, his somewhat defensive reaction to her suggestion had given her more ammunition.

'We could make it a foursome,' she said. 'Or maybe not. How about a nice little restaurant where you could wine and dine her? The Griffin just outside Abergavenny is nice.'

'So is the chip shop in the high street,' he retorted. 'It's about all I can afford at the moment.'

'Are things that bad?'

'I used every penny I had to pay the deposit on my place,' he said. 'Then there were the solicitor's fees. And my last few wage packets went on getting the roof repaired. I'm skint, broke, brassic, without funds—'

'OK, OK,' she laughed. 'You could always take her on a picnic. I could let you have a loaf of bread and a pork pie or two.'

'Very funny. What you could do is let me know when you want to see Edie next.'

'Shhh! I swear to God that Julia's got every room in this bloody mansion bugged. I'll text you. I'm waiting for her to come back to me with the mock-up, but when she does, I'll be sure to let you know.'

Her smirk was quite infuriating, and James narrowed his eyes at her.

'Are you glad to be back?' she asked him, suddenly serious. 'It must be so different here.'

His answer was slow in coming, as he thought about his response. 'It was time,' he said. 'The big stuff was fun, like the reintroduction of wolves in some parts of the US – that was my last big project, and it's ongoing – but I'm needed back here. William's done the donkey work with the beavers, but I'm hoping to take it one step further.'

'In what way?'

'We've known for a long time that the dams beavers build slow down the rate at which upstream rainfall enters the main rivers, but my work is to provide concrete, statistical evidence and present it to the various authorities. Our climate in the UK is set to become warmer and wetter, with more storms and increased precipitation, which in turn will put even greater pressure on our waterways. Flooding will become more commonplace, and with so many people living on the flood plains…'

'I get the picture,' Tia said, 'and I admire what you're trying to do.' Her expression turned playful. 'This had better not mean you've not got any time for luurve.' She drew out the last word and simpered.

James sighed. She was incorrigible, but it was lovely to see. He knew how hard it had been for her after the accident, and to have her all loved-up, happy and enthusiastic about life was a delight. William was a very lucky man, and James envied him. One day he wanted to be married with a home of his own filled with children and laughter.

He'd made a start on the home bit. But the wife and kids bit would take some doing.

Then the image of Edie and her delightful little boy leapt into his mind. Oh dear: it looked like he was totally and utterly smitten.

Maybe a picnic wasn't such a bad idea, after all.

Chapter 9

The text was from James and it said, *I know it might be difficult to talk, so can you call me when you've got a chance?*

Edie wondered what this was about. She hoped Tia hadn't changed her mind about anything major. Time was getting on and the wedding was only a couple of months away. This wouldn't normally be a problem, but Edie was having to work on the gown in between working on the stuff she was being paid to do by Mrs C. She had so little time as it was and Tia's commission put added pressure on her, even without the bride changing her mind.

Stevie Taylor from Peggy's Tea Shoppe was due in today to have a proper fitting, but maybe she'd find the time to call James afterwards. The Buckingham dress sample had looked gorgeous on Miss Taylor, but now it was time for the bride to try on the bespoke gown. There was still a great deal of work to be done on it, but the basics were there, and Edie wanted to ensure that the dress was a perfect fit before she moved forward with it.

In the meantime, she had a lot to be going on with, and the first thing she needed to do was to check out some fabric samples for Tia. The shop had a comprehensive selection of swatches and she spent the next hour trawling through them, finally identifying three shades of grey silk georgette which she thought Tia might like, and a couple of possibilities for the silver over-fabric. She was reluctant to do this on Mrs C's time, and did briefly consider taking them home with her at the end of the day, but the swatches needed sorting out anyway, and checking that each individual one was still part of the company's current stock was something she did on a monthly basis; she justified it to herself by the fact that she was killing two birds with one stone.

Then she spent some more time choosing the beads and pearls that she hoped Tia would approve of.

Just as she'd finished doing that, Mrs Carrington informed her that Miss Taylor had arrived, and she hurried downstairs with the bride's half-finished dress.

'Just as I thought,' Mrs Carrington said when Miss Taylor stood in front of them clad in the beautiful gown.

Edie circled the bride, gently tugging and pulling, several pins in her mouth, as she checked and double-checked the fit.

It was perfect; only a minor adjustment was needed around the bust, but otherwise there was little that needed to be done to the basic structure.

She carefully helped Miss Taylor out of the gown and put it to one side. She'd take it back up to her workroom later, and hopefully complete the alteration by the end of the day. Before that, she had to work on Tia's dress – the one Lady Tonbridge was insisting on. It seemed such a waste of time, effort and material, but to do anything less would only invite comment, censure and possibly even suspicion.

It was much later, after she'd collected Danny from her mother, helped him with his homework (which was numeracy today), made them both dinner, and had sat with him while he designed and painted a mask for school, that she found the time to call James.

'Hi, it's Edie,' she said when he answered, and her heart did an odd little thump when she heard his voice.

'Edie,' he said, 'I'm glad you called.'

She asked, worriedly, 'Is everything all right?'

'Of course it is.'

'It's just that I thought I was going to phone Tia when I had something for her.'

'It's not about Tia.'

'No?'

'It's… er… I, um wondered if you'd, um, like to go out. With me. For a picnic.'

'With you?' Gosh, she hadn't been expecting that.

'Yes, with me.'

She heard a smile in his tone and she found herself smiling back, glad that he couldn't see her face.

'I'm not sure,' she said. As much as she liked him, and thought him a really nice guy, she didn't want to encourage him. He was way out of her league and she guessed he probably had women falling over themselves to date him. More suitable women, the type he was more used to. The rich type, who didn't have to scrimp and save, and who didn't have a young son. Socialites, she thought they were called, the sort of girls who'd gone to private schools, and attended parties and balls, and who spent inordinate amounts of money in beauty parlours and hairdressers, and who were clothed in the latest fashion from exclusive stores. Much like William Ferris's sister, Melissa.

Tia hadn't been born into such privilege, Edie knew, but with her brother Nick being a wealthy and successful showjumper, Tia was now in the same league. Even if she wasn't, Edie guessed that Tia Saunders could hold her own and not be intimidated by those rich girls. William Ferris loved her, and that was all that mattered.

Edie, on the other hand, didn't want to start something that would end in heartache. She was probably nothing more than a novelty for James, and once he grew bored of her plain, unassuming lifestyle, he'd go back to where he belonged.

'I don't think so,' she said, 'but thank you for the offer. I've got Danny to consider.'

'Oh. OK. Um, it was just a thought… I'll let you get on. I'm sure you're busy.'

She was. Very. Which was another reason why she didn't need a casual fling right now. She didn't have the time or the energy for one. As handsome and as attractive as James was, and as flattered as she was that he'd asked her out, she felt it best to refuse; she didn't need that sort of complication in her life, right now. If ever.

It was only later, when she was running a deep, hot bath, that something occurred to her. He'd asked her to go for a picnic, not dinner, as would be far more usual for a date, so maybe he didn't want to be seen in public with her.

And on that note, she pushed James Preece firmly out of her mind. If she wasn't good enough to be taken to a restaurant, then she certainly wasn't going to sit in a field with him while he made a pass at her!

Chapter 10

That went well, James thought sarcastically. She'd made it pretty clear she wasn't interested in him, and he felt quite deflated. He'd been turned down by other girls in the past, of course, but this rejection was the only one he couldn't seem to shake off. He kept thinking about her, even though it was hopeless, and it annoyed the hell out of him.

Suck it up and move on, he told himself, but yet again, the memory of his very first sight of her kept popping into his mind. She'd been so shy and guarded, appearing almost fearful, that his heart had gone out to her, and he'd wanted nothing more than to gather her into him and tell her everything would be all right.

He knew her a tiny bit better now, and he realised that she wasn't as timid and nervous as she'd first seemed. She had a mind of her own, as her agreement to make Tia a wedding dress proved.

Why she'd refused him, he had no idea. If there hadn't been that little spark between them, then he would have assumed that she wasn't attracted to him. But there had been, he was certain of it.

Or maybe he'd read it wrong.

Cross with himself, he decided to take a stroll around his property.

His property!

It sounded an awful lot grander than it was. He was the proud owner of a semi-derelict farmhouse and a couple of acres of overgrown land. But he didn't care. It was his, and if it took him the next ten years to do it up and make it into a home, then so be it. He had time. Lots of it. Because he was living from wage packet to wage packet, improvements were rather on the slow side. Each month he waited until he got paid, then decided what he could afford to spend on making the place habitable. He intended to do most of the work himself, and what he wasn't able to do, like the rewiring, he'd save up for until he could afford to employ an electrician to do it for him.

At least he'd made the roof leakproof, although at some stage further down the line, he'd need to replace it altogether. And he had electricity (despite the fact that it was a bit dodgy) and the plumbing worked (although that was equally dodgy). He had a workable kitchen, basic and extremely old, although the butler sink was an original and he intended to keep the ancient black-leaded range as a feature. Not to actually cook with, though; he'd want a proper oven and hob for that.

The house had a scullery, which he intended to turn into a utility room at some point; a boot room where coats and muddy Wellington boots could live; a decent-sized dining room; another room which could be used as a study or an office; and a large living room with an open fireplace and elderly built-in cupboards that were past their best, but which the estate agent had called a 'period feature'. The house also had four double bedrooms upstairs, one of them with a large cupboard off it that could eventually be an en-suite. There was an awfully long way to go before that happened, though.

Thankfully, the place was structurally sound, although he did need to knock the walls back to the bare brick and re-plaster all the inside. His main concern for the moment was to repoint the exterior and replace all the doors and windows, one at a time, when he'd learnt how to make and fit them. And after that, he intended to install a small wind turbine and solar panels, so he wasn't reliant on power from the national grid.

But it was the outside that James had fallen in love with. All that lovely space where he could experiment with eco-farming in his planned vegetable plot. Most of the rest of the land would be set aside for wildlife, although he intended to keep chickens and maybe a goat. He liked goats, and they were the ultimate compost bins as they'd eat almost anything. In fact, he'd planned to borrow a small herd to eat all the brush, briars and other plants where his vegetable garden and orchard would eventually go – they'd be a lot quicker and more efficient than if he tried to clear the land himself, and they'd fertilise the soil at the same time. After the goats would come the pigs. There was nothing like a determined pig to rootle through the soil and churn it up. Although, at this precise moment in time, he had no clue where to borrow a pig or two from...

It was beginning to get dark, summer not yet at its zenith, but the temperature was warm enough to venture outside wearing only a fleece. He donned his sturdy boots and slipped out of the boot room door, not bothering to lock it behind him. Tanglewood was that sort of place, although if he lived in the heart of the village, he probably would have dropped the latch before he left. But this far out, he'd be impressed if he saw anyone at all, except for maybe that new ranger, Rex, who was dating Leanne who owned the flower shop, or Geoff Green, a nearby farmer and Leanne's father, and he trusted both of them implicitly. Besides, if anyone did slink around looking for mischief and things to steal, then they'd be very disappointed indeed with his meagre possessions.

He breathed deeply, his nose filled with the scents of green, growing things, like the ferns coating the valley sides and the heather from the mountains higher up the slopes. With eyes quickly becoming attuned to the twilight, he paced around the perimeter of the property, noting where he thought the drystone walls needed repairing. Although, he realised, he'd need fencing around the planned vegetable garden to keep the rabbits out, and he'd have to have a proper coop and run for the chickens. He wanted them to wander freely during the day, but at night they'd have to be secured, to keep them safe from foxes.

There was one now, barking close by. The cubs would be out of the den at this time of year, and well on their way to becoming independent. A chicken would be a tasty, easy meal for them if he wasn't careful.

Low bleats sounded beyond the walls and he could hear the occasional cough of a ewe, sounding like an old man, which made him smile. The evening was so still, he could even hear grass being torn as the animals grazed.

A few minutes later, a rustle nearby caught his attention and he peered into the gloom, wondering if it was the fox he'd just heard, or perhaps a hedgehog. Hedgehogs weren't the stealthiest of creatures and they tended to trundle about in an unconcerned manner as they rooted for worms and grubs.

Movement, quick and bouncing, beyond the wall, made him freeze. Not a fox or a hedgehog, but rabbits. Lots of them. They'd probably been spooked by Mr Fox and were only now cautiously venturing out of their bolt-holes, all swivelling ears and twitching noses. Not that he could see their noses, but he guessed what they'd be doing.

Hang on, was that a lamb among them? If it was, it was very small. It must be a late birthing, he thought, as the majority of ewes had given birth around three months ago. He didn't know a great deal about sheep, despite having grown up not far from Tanglewood in an area where sheep farming was prevalent, but he did know that this little fellow was too young to be so far away from his mum, the rest of the sheep having wandered away.

It was tiny – really, really tiny, and sort of oddly hunched; it moved strangely too, as if it was injured, or was on the ground and trying to get to its feet.

Should he attempt to catch it? And it would be an attempt, too, because lambs were quick little things when they had to be. But if he didn't try, then there was a good chance that the fox might take advantage of the lack of a mother and decide it would have lamb for supper.

As quietly as he could, James scaled the four-foot-high wall, taking extra care when clambering over the upended and pointy coping stones, trying not to catch his foot on one of them.

When he was safely over, he sank to his knees on the damp grass. Dew was already forming on the stems and soon his jeans were wet, but he ignored the cold seeping through the cloth and inched forward.

The lamb was firmly ensconced in the middle of the rabbits, obviously thinking that the company of bunnies was preferable to no company at all, and James felt sorry for the little creature.

Another couple of inches forward, and although it was almost fully dark, now that he'd managed to get close enough to see the animal clearer, he bit his lip to stop himself from laughing out loud.

It wasn't a lamb.

It was a rabbit. A white one, and as out of place on the mountainside as a fish would be. OK, that was an exaggeration, but it didn't alter the fact that a white rabbit's chances of survival were slim. Wild rabbits were a brown-grey colour for a reason – camouflage. Either this one was a natural aberration, or it was a tame rabbit which had either escaped or had been set free.

If the latter was the case, he wondered how long the poor little chap had been living out here. It was a miracle he hadn't been eaten; white stood out like a sore thumb in the wild, especially for animals who were most active at dawn and twilight, and were at the top of every predators' menu.

He debated whether to leave the rabbit be and let nature take its course, but he simply couldn't abandon it to its fate. He was realistic enough to realise he didn't stand a chance of catching it, but he had to try. If the rabbit had formerly been a pet, then it might let him get close enough to touch it. On the other hand, it might take one look at him and scarper.

Not wanting to scare the life out of it by rugby tackling it as soon as he was in range, he began to make soft noises. A flick of an ear in his direction told him the bunny knew

73

he was there. The fact that the rest of the bunch fled the moment they caught sight of him was also a bit of a give-away. But his rabbit held its ground, to James's surprise, so he continued to creep forwards, one hand stretched out in what he hoped the creature would consider to be a friendly manner.

'Hello, little one,' he crooned. 'Where have you come from? I wonder if there's a little boy or girl missing you right at this very moment.' He was talking nonsense, he knew, but it wasn't as if the rabbit could understand him. He just needed to keep talking to it.

The ears flicked and swivelled, but the bunny stayed put, and eventually James got to within a couple of feet – almost close enough to touch, but not quite. And there he stayed for a few more minutes, talking to the little animal and letting it get used to him. Then, when he felt the time was right, he inched a little closer and reached out until his fingers touched the soft fur.

The rabbit shuffled a bit, but it didn't hop away. Encouraged, James moved a fraction closer, until he wasn't just touching the rabbit, he was actually stroking it, and the bunny seemed perfectly content to let him. It even lifted its head and rubbed its whiskery face against his palm.

This little thing had been a well-handled and dearly loved pet, he thought.

Gently and very slowly, he reached out his other hand and lifted the rabbit into his arms, cuddling it against his chest. The animal snuggled into him, its head underneath his chin, its whiskers tickling his skin. As he held it, he realised it was very thin, and that its ears were torn. It had probably been fighting, and, as rabbits had a hierar-chical society, he guessed this one might have been on the bottom of the pile. The others may well have picked on it unmercifully. Besides that, despite its natural instincts, if it was someone's pet, then it wouldn't have had much of a clue about how to be a wild rabbit.

Whatever had happened to it, it seemed mighty pleased to see him.

He'd take it home and once it had been fed and watered, he'd rig up a secure place for it to sleep. Tomorrow, he'd ask around and see if anyone had lost a white bunny and hope that someone would claim it.

If no one did, then he didn't know what he was going to do with—

Actually, he *did* know. There was a certain little boy who'd be only too thrilled at owning a rabbit, especially one as loving as this one appeared to be. He understood Danny wasn't allowed a dog or a cat, but surely an outdoor pet would be acceptable? And it didn't need walking either.

James hoped no one would come forward. Not only did every child deserve to have a pet, but it would also give him an excuse to see Edie again. And that was something he most definitely wanted to do.

Chapter 11

'I've… um… got something for Danny,' James said, as Edie answered the door to his unexpected knock. 'I hope you don't mind,' he added.

When she saw the worried and rather sheepish look on his face, she wondered what on earth it could be. 'What is it?'

'It's a rabbit.'

Edie froze, wondering if she'd heard him correctly. If she had, while she appreciated the gesture, Danny was a trifle old for cuddly toys. He'd never been into them in the first place, except when he was tiny, much preferring cars and wooden blocks (he was starting to become interested in computer games, but she was trying to keep a lid on that for as long as she could).

'I fully understand if you say no,' James continued, 'but I know how much he wants a pet, and considering a dog or a cat is out of the question and fish, although interesting to look at, don't do an awful lot, and hamsters tend to sleep during the day, and this little fella was out in the wild when he's clearly someone's pet, and—'

'Wait, are you trying to tell me you're giving him a real live rabbit?'

'Er… yes.'

'Not a stuffed one?'

'No, it's alive, all right. I found it on the mountain behind my house and took it home.'

Edie was flabbergasted. 'You mean, it's a *wild* rabbit?'

'Not at all. It's used to being handled and it's very friendly.'

'How could you tell?' What she meant to ask was, did James usually make a habit of kidnapping animals from the wild and taking them home with him? Is this what the gentry did these days instead of shooting them? It was totally bizarre.

'Come and see,' he said, gesturing towards the arched entrance to the courtyard and the high street beyond.

'Don't tell me you've brought it with you?' she asked, incredulously.

His smile became even more bashful. 'Yeah…'

'Why would you do such a thing?'

'I can't keep it, but I thought Danny might be able to.'

She followed him out to his car, shaking her head. Thank God Danny was with her mum, otherwise she'd have her work cut out when she informed him that they couldn't possibly accept the gift of a rabbit. As it was, she'd have to swear James to secrecy, because if Danny ever got to know of it, she wouldn't hear the end of it.

A rabbit was one thing, but she'd have to buy a hutch, the food, the bowls, then there were the potential vet bills… No, she had enough claims on her limited finances as it was, without adding to them.

Curiosity got the better of her, though, and despite her reluctance, she found herself following him out of the courtyard and into the street.

Sure enough, James had a snow-white bunny in the back of his car, safely tucked away inside a cat carrier. But to her surprise, there was also a large hutch, which James had stowed in the back (he'd had to put the rear seats down to fit it in), and a bag of hay.

'I can't accept this,' she told him. 'It's a lovely thought and I do appreciate it, but…'

His face fell. 'Oh dear. I'll just have to see if I can find someone else to take her in.'

'Can't you put her back where you found her?' she asked.

'If I did, she wouldn't last long. For one thing, she's the wrong colour – I don't know how long she'd been out there, but it can't have been more than a few days, a week at the most. Wild rabbits are brown for a reason; it helps camouflage them. A fox or a falcon would spot her a mile off. Then there's the fact that rabbits have a social structure, and I'd bet my right arm that she's at the bottom of it. Her ears are torn, which shows she's been fighting, and she was probably picked on by the other rabbits. She's all skin and bone, possibly from stress; rabbits don't do well when they're stressed.'

'That's not fair – now you've got me feeling sorry for her.'

He chuckled, a deep rumbling sound that sent shivers through her. 'That's my intention,' he said. 'Look at her; how can you resist that little face?'

He had a point, she conceded; the rabbit was exceptionally cute. But he wouldn't change her mind – there wasn't any room in her and Danny's lives for a pet. Who would end up looking after it? She would, of course. She barely had any spare time as it was, without having to take care of a rabbit, however sweet it was.

'Have you tried to find its owner?' she asked.

78

James looked shocked. 'Of course I have. I've even taken her to the vet, just in case she's been microchipped. That's how I knew she was a girl – the vet told me. Apparently, it's rather difficult to sex a rabbit if you don't know what you're doing.'

'And you don't?'

He shook his head. 'I've not had an awful lot to do with rabbits. What I do know, though, is that she's very loving and is used to being handled. She'd make a wonderful first pet for a small boy, and she'd live outside, and wouldn't take a great deal of looking after. It would teach him responsibility and empathy and—'

Edie threw her hands up in the air. 'OK, OK, you win,' she said. 'We'll take her in, but I warn you, if Danny doesn't pull his weight, I'll be giving you a call.'

'It's a deal.' James held out his hand, and she took it.

Another bolt of electricity shot through her when his palm wrapped around hers, and she snatched her hand back swiftly. That wouldn't do at all. He was starting to get under her skin, which was something she didn't want and wasn't prepared for. If she didn't have time for a rabbit, she certainly didn't have time for a man in her life, no matter if he was almost as cute as the bunny.

James carried the hutch through her cottage and into the little yard at the back. She offered to give him a hand, but he refused, so she stood back and let him get on with it, trying not to look at the play of muscles under his shirt as he hefted the bulk of the hutch.

'There's a separate run,' he said, jerking his head towards a bundle of poles with mesh attached to them, 'so she'll have plenty of room.'

We'll see about that, Edie thought, picturing the small space outside her back door. And she was right. With the hutch and run installed, there was barely enough space left for her tubs, and the small table and the pair of chairs which graced the yard.

He set the contraption up, ensuring it was secure, then went back to the car to fetch the rabbit and the hay he'd brought with him, spreading the bedding evenly over the floor of the hutch.

'Oh, I've also got this,' he said, handing her a carrier bag.

Edie took a peep at the contents. Inside were two bowls, a bag of food, a water bottle, a selection of treats and a couple of items which gave her pause; one of them looked like a cat's litter tray, and the other appeared to be an extremely small harness, the type that a dog might wear. There was also a lead attached to it.

She gave James a curious look.

'Rabbits are extremely easy to house-train, so the vet told me, and they can also be taken for walks on a lead,' he said.

Edie didn't know what to think about that. A rabbit living outside was one thing; a rabbit living in the house was an altogether different proposition. And as for taking it for a walk… she simply couldn't envisage a bunny hopping on a lead next to her. It was ludicrous, to say the least.

'Oh, and she's been vaccinated against myxomatosis and she's been neutered,' James added.

'You appear to have thought of everything.'

'There's no point in giving half a gift, is there?' he countered. 'Right then, now that she's settled, shall we get going? Tia'll be wondering where we are. That reminds me, I take it Danny's not here?'

Edie shook her head. 'Luckily for you, he's at my mother's. Can you imagine if he'd been at home and I'd said no to the rabbit?' She caught sight of his expression. 'You sneaky thing! You were hoping he'd be here, weren't you, so I couldn't say no without looking like a bad egg.'

He held up his hands. 'Guilty as charged,' he said, and Edie sent him an exasperated look.

'You won't regret it, I promise,' he added. 'Kids deserve to have pets. It's good for their emotional development.'

Hmph!

All the way to The Furlongs, the only thing Edie could think about was Danny's face when he saw the rabbit. He'd be over the moon. She still wasn't convinced it was a good idea and, even with the get-out clause of James taking the rabbit back if things didn't work out, she knew she'd have a fight on her hands to persuade Danny to relinquish it.

Oh dear, what had she let herself in for?

At least Tia was pleased with the progress of her dress. Even at this early stage, she was thrilled with the cut, the fit and the flow. The scooped neckline showed off her delicate shoulders and collarbone, and emphasised her long neck. Edie intended to pay as much attention to the detailing on the back as she did the front. Was it Mrs C or Lady Tonbridge who'd said no one would see the back of it? They were wrong. Maybe the lower part of the bodice wouldn't be visible, but the top half certainly would, especially since Tia intended to wear her hair up.

The skirt draped elegantly over her legs, cascading down to her ankles in a silken waterfall, and the choice of fabric meant that it wouldn't need constant adjustment every time Tia moved.

James had made himself scarce the moment they'd arrived, clearly not enamoured with talk of seed pearls and diamantes, but he reappeared after an hour to check on progress and Tia noticed that Danny wasn't with him.

'I managed to persuade my mum to have him for a couple of hours,' Edie said to her, after James disappeared again with instructions to come back in fifteen minutes. 'It was a good job, as it happened,' she added.

'Oh, why's that?'

'James gave Danny a rabbit and bought him everything to go with it, even a damned harness to take it for a walk.'

Tia burst out laughing. 'Oh, my, that's hilarious. Fancy taking a bunny for a walk. Or should I say, a hop?'

'I'm glad you find it amusing,' Edie said, dryly.

'Did you accept his generous gift?' Tia wanted to know.

'I did, as a matter of fact, because he guilted me into it. But imagine if I hadn't and Danny had been at home? He'd have hated me forever.'

Tia laughed again, then sobered. 'James is a good man,' she said. 'I've only known him since he returned to the UK, but William spoke about him a lot. They've been best friends since school. He says you won't find a better bloke.'

Edie nearly said that she didn't want to find *any* bloke, but she held her tongue. Her private life was her concern and no one else's, and Tia was a paying client, no matter how friendly she was. It wouldn't do to become too familiar.

Talk of the devil, and there he was; James strolled into the living room, all casual confidence and as sexy as hell.

Wait. *What?* Did she just think of James as sexy?

Oh, dear. She'd have to stop this nonsense right now. She really mustn't think of James as sexy, because she was in danger of developing a mighty big girly crush on the guy.

She resolved to be on the polite side of friendly to him, and nothing more, but that vow went straight out of the window when he asked her if he could please be there when Danny saw the rabbit for the first time.

'It's not that I want or expect any thanks,' he hastened to say. 'It's just that I'd love to see the expression on his face when he realises he's got a pet of his very own.'

How could she refuse him?

'Of course,' she said. 'I'll have to stop off at my mum's to collect him first, though.'

'No problem. Just tell me where she lives.'

'Not far from me, in Warren Street, funnily enough.'

He chuckled, getting the reference immediately. 'See,' he said. 'The rabbit was meant to be.'

'Hmm.' She still wasn't totally convinced, but she had to admit that she was looking forward to seeing her son's reaction, too. Quietly excited, she told James to pull over outside her mum's and got out of the car.

'He's just eaten his tea,' her mum said, as Edie knocked and walked straight in. 'Shall I put the kettle on?'

Edie usually stayed for a short while whenever she collected Danny. Her mum enjoyed catching up with her and as a rule Edie did, too. But not today.

'I can't stop, Mum,' she said. 'There's someone waiting for me.'

'Is it that Tia girl you've been telling me about?'

'No, it's James, the guy who's been driving me back and forth to The Furlongs.'

She saw the inquisitive expression on her mum's face, and added, 'It's nothing like that – he's got a surprise for Danny, that's all.'

'For me?' Her son appeared at her elbow, his eyes bright with curiosity.

'Yes, for you,' she laughed.

'What is it?'

'If I told you, it wouldn't be a surprise, would it?'

'Aww…' He bounced around, already excited.

He'd be unstoppable once he saw what was waiting for him at home, she realised.

Her mother raised her eyebrows. 'And you say it's nothing like that,' she said.

'It isn't. Look, I've got to dash, and I don't want to spoil the surprise for Danny, so I'll phone you later, OK?'

Edie could tell that her mother was almost about to explode and was dying to know what the surprise was, too, but her mum nodded.

'Go and get your things,' Edie said to Danny. 'James is waiting outside.'

'Is he going to take me riding again?'

'Not today, but I promise that the next time I visit Tia, you can come with me.'

That seemed to satisfy him for the moment, and he scampered into the living room to fetch his little rucksack.

He could hardly contain himself on the short drive to their house, and neither could James, if the expression on his face was anything to go by. Edie was full of anticipation, too, and as soon as the car drew to a halt, she was out of the passenger seat and helping Danny out of the back before James had even turned the engine off.

'What is it?' Danny cried, hopping up and down as they walked through the courtyard and she fished her keys out of her bag. He shot inside, his eyes darting around the neat little living room.

'Out the back,' she said, leading the way into the kitchen and unlocking the door to the yard.

At first, Danny didn't realise what he was looking at, then a little white form hopped slowly from the rear of the hutch and he saw the rabbit.

For a second, he was quiet, almost thoughtful. 'Is it a rabbit?' he asked.

'Yep,' James said, a huge grin on his face.

'Is it mine?'

'Yep.'

Danny looked to her for confirmation and she nodded. 'But it's only yours if you promise to look after it properly. You'll need to feed her every day, check that she's got plenty of water, clean her hutch out and give her treats, like carrots, to eat.'

'Will she live out here?' he asked. 'What about when it's cold and wet?'

'Then you'll have to put down extra bedding for her,' James said, glancing at Edie out of the corner of his eye, no doubt thinking about the litter tray he'd provided, but wise enough not to say anything.

Edie left James to explain to her son all about the correct care for the rabbit, and went to put the kettle on. When she came back out bearing two cups of coffee (she hoped James drank coffee, and didn't have a penchant for Earl Grey tea, or something similar) she found the pair of them kneeling on the ground, Danny with the rabbit snuggled happily in his arms, an expression of total bliss on his little face. They were busy discussing names.

'How about one from Peter Rabbit or *Watership Down*?' James suggested. 'Like Bramble or Heather?'

'Mary,' Danny said decisively, and Edie turned away to hide her smile. She'd already known what Danny was going to call her.

While her son cooed over Mary, James and Edie sat on the two little chairs and sipped their drinks.

'Thanks for letting me see this,' James said quietly. 'It means a lot to me.'

She eyed him surreptitiously – he appeared to be sincere. Which made the answer to the question he asked her next a great deal harder than it should have been.

'Will you go out for a meal with me?' he asked. 'I was thinking of the Duke's Arms.'

For a minute, she was sorely tempted. How bad could it be? She was sure she'd have a good time. He was, as Tia said, a really nice guy, but that was part of the problem. If he'd been a player, and if she'd suspected he'd given Danny the rabbit solely to get into her knickers, then she'd have no qualms whatsoever about turning him down.

She didn't say anything for a moment, letting him know she was taking his question seriously. Then she said, 'I'm sorry, but I don't think that's a good idea.'

He didn't, as she expected him to, ask why not. Instead, he said, 'If you change your mind, the offer will still be there. I really like you, Edie Adams.'

Unfortunately, she also liked him, too. And that was definitely the problem.

Chapter 12

William allowed James to straighten his tie, but the groom appeared impatient to be off, not enjoying being measured and fitted for his wedding suit, and particularly not enjoying having to pick out a tie.

'For a toff who's used to wearing this kind of stuff, you're hopeless,' he said to the groom.

'I hate wearing a tie,' William grumbled, tugging at it.

James slapped his hand away. 'Stop fussing with it; you'll get finger marks all over it. It's not made out of the same awful material the school ties were made out of. If you're not careful, you'll ruin it.'

William gave him an incredulous look. 'Since when did you become so knowledgeable about fabric?' He paused, then a wide grin spread slowly across his face. 'Oh, I get it.'

James feigned ignorance. 'I've no idea what you're talking about,' he replied loftily.

'I'm right!' William was positively crowing, but at least it had stopped him tugging at his tie as though it was a hangman's noose around his neck and not the finest silk the bespoke tailor had to offer.

'You've been talking to that little seamstress, haven't you?' William said. 'Tia said she thought you liked her when you saw her at The Manor the other week. You crafty dog. Go on, spill the beans.'

'There aren't any beans to spill,' he said.

'I'm so glad you don't play poker. You'd be bankrupt in a week.'

'I'm bankrupt anyway,' he said, dryly. 'I've finally just about got enough in my bank account to pay for the house to be rewired. Thank God your mother takes pity on me and feeds me now and again. Beans on toast doesn't half become boring after a while. Remember that muck they used to serve up in the school dining hall every Thursday? Shepherd's pie, my backside! They ought to have been done under the Trade Descriptions Act – unless, of course, the swill that they claimed was minced beef actually *was* a shepherd—'

'Stop trying to change the subject.'

'I'm not!' James protested, but it sounded false, and both of them knew it.

'You really like her, don't you?' William persisted.

James was about to deny any such thing, but decided against any further protests. William knew him too well – he could read him as clearly as the proverbial book. Trying to hide anything from his best and oldest friend was a waste of time and effort. Besides, he realised he *wanted* to talk about her, about his failure to get her even to go out for a meal with him.

'Yes, I do,' he admitted with a heartfelt sigh. 'But the problem is, I don't think she likes me.'

'Of course she does! Who doesn't like you?'

'Edie Adams, that's who. Although I did think there was a spark, but I must have imagined it.'

William sobered instantly. 'I didn't realise you were interested in anyone. You kept that quiet.'

'If anything happens, you'll be the first to know,' he promised.

'So, tell me all about it.' William urged.

James thought carefully about what he was going to say. Tia had sworn him to secrecy; she'd not even told her husband-to-be of her intention to wear a different dress to the one his mother was planning, and if he said the wrong thing, he could totally land himself in it. Tia would tear him to shreds; she might be little, but she had a fierce temper.

'I sort of bumped into Edie, we got chatting, and I asked her if she'd like to go on a picnic.'

William barked out a laugh. 'A picnic! You're kidding, right?'

'What's wrong with that? I can't exactly afford an à la carte meal. I can barely afford a pork pie and an egg and cress sarnie. But I did suggest going for a meal at the Duke's Arms and she turned me down then, too.'

'Look, mate, you've got to make an impression, and a picnic or steak and chips down the local watering hole just don't cut it. You're not going to get anyone to go out on a date with you if that's all you're offering. You need to do some proper wining and dining. You have to woo her, make her realise how special she is.'

'It's all right for you – I don't exactly have the same financial assets as you. I did give her son a rabbit, though.'

William spluttered. 'A rabbit! Are you having a laugh?'

'No, I'm serious. I found a rabbit, and—'

'You didn't even *buy* it! Oh, my God, that's hilarious. Most guys buy their girls roses. I've never heard of anyone trying to impress a girl with a rabbit before!'

James thought William might have a heart attack, he was laughing so hard.

'Can we get back to the suit fitting, please?' he asked. 'I've got a man coming about a septic tank in a couple of hours.'

'Please don't tell your seamstress about your septic tank problems,' William begged, tears streaming down his face. 'You wait until I tell Tia about all this.'

James had to bite back the retort that Tia already knew a fair bit about what was going on in his love life. Or, should he say, lack of it…

He knew he should cut his losses and walk away, but that was easier said than done, because he still had a few more sessions of ferrying Edie back and forth to The Furlongs, so he'd have to see her, whether he wanted to or not. And he did want to – he really, really did. Never had a girl got under his skin the way Edie had.

He made a pact with himself: if she still hadn't agreed to a date by the time Tia's wedding dress was finished, then he'd throw in the towel and give up pursuing her. He had a few more weeks in which to convince her.

But maybe William was right, and it was time to pull out all the stops and bugger the expense.

Chapter 13

Edie couldn't believe she was actually doing this. Never in a million years had she imagined herself taking a large white rabbit out for a walk. But once Danny had realised it was a possibility, he'd nagged her until she'd given in.

She didn't normally acquiesce to repeated demands from her son and she hoped she wasn't setting a precedent, but it hadn't seemed such an unreasonable request when she'd had time to get used to the idea. After all, she'd heard of cats being taken for walks on a lead, so why not rabbits? Aside from the obvious, that no one else to her knowledge had ever dragged a rabbit across the field down by the river before.

Steeled for some odd looks, Edie lifted Mary out of her hutch, marvelling at the softness of the rabbit's fur, and, after a few false starts, managed to strap the little creature into her harness. To Edie's surprise, the rabbit didn't seem at all bothered. She really was a sweet-natured little thing. Danny had only owned her for a few days, but already she could see the bond developing between the two of them. The rabbit looked for him every morning (although, Edie conceded, it might be because that was when he fed her), and the little boy and his pet always spent a happy half-hour together before Danny had to get ready for school.

No longer did she have to fight to get him out of bed in the morning; she used the lure of the rabbit to persuade him to eat his breakfast, wash his face, and brush his hair before he was allowed to see to Mary. She did still have a bit of a tussle to get him into his school uniform, because she left that until the last minute, not wanting him to get it covered in tiny white hairs, but she could cope with that.

'I'll carry her along the high street, shall I, then put her down when we get to the field?' Edie went to pick Mary up, but Danny asked if he could carry her.

'If you're sure,' Edie said doubtfully. Mary might be small, but after a while, Edie guessed the rabbit might start to feel quite heavy, especially to a small boy.

'I want to do it,' Danny insisted. 'You said it's my responsibility to look after her, so that's what I'm doing.'

She had to admire his dedication, but she'd see how he felt in a little while. After all, Danny wasn't very big himself, and carrying a rabbit for any distance would take a bit of doing.

Her son surprised her. She could see the effort it cost him to carry Mary from their house, down the high street, and to the gate leading to the path along the riverbank, by the way he leaned back to balance the rabbit's weight and the grim determination on his face. It was then she began to think that maybe James knew what he was talking about. Danny was learning that taking responsibility for something was sometimes hard work, but it still had to be done.

She also saw something else in her son's eyes – determination and pride. With his head held high, he ignored the double-takes, the astonished comments, and the fuss and attention his rabbit was getting, and he strode down the street towards the river and the lovely open fields flanking it. He was behaving as though taking a rabbit for a stroll was an everyday occurrence.

And in time it might become exactly that, but for now it was a novelty, both for her and Danny and the rest of the villagers, who were much more used to seeing bunnies in hutches than wearing a harness and hopping along behind their owners. She wasn't sure whether being taken for a walk was a novelty for the rabbit or not. The way Mary was behaving, Edie suspected that this wasn't the rabbit's first outing.

Edie prayed it wouldn't turn out to be its last.

The first part of the walk was uneventful, with Edie and Danny walking slowly along the path next to the river, giving Mary plenty of time to hop and sniff. Whenever they encountered a dog, Edie would scoop Mary up to keep her out of harm's way, just in case. None of the dogs appeared to be unduly interested, but she felt Mary stiffen in her arms whenever one of them came too close.

Looking at the absolute joy on her son's face, she wished she'd bought him a pet sooner. A rabbit was an excellent choice because it could live outdoors, and this one seemed perfectly happy being taken for a walk – almost like a token dog – so they had the best of both worlds in a way.

'Mum, James said the bunny can also come indoors to be played with because she can be trained to use a litter tray,' Danny informed her, almost as if he knew what she was thinking. His little face was full of hope.

'We'll see.' Her reply was non-committal. The rules of her tenancy agreement stated that she wasn't allowed any pets. Bringing Mary indoors would seriously contravene them. Besides, she didn't know how she felt about having a rabbit in the house; although if Mary could be trained to use a litter tray, it would solve the problem of little accidents everywhere and, unlike a cat, it wouldn't climb or scratch its claws on her precious fabrics, and neither would it need taking for a walk, like a dog would. However, she still had to be convinced that any animal at all was a good idea; the novelty of taking care of his pet might soon wear off, but she was prepared to give him the benefit of the doubt for the time being.

'Mum?'

'Yes, Danny?' From the tone of his voice, she suspected that he was about to ask her for something he knew she was going to refuse.

'Is James your boyfriend now?'

Ooh, she hadn't been expecting that! 'No, poppet, he isn't. What makes you think he is?'

'Because he bought me Mary.'

Edie didn't contradict him, because a part of her actually did wonder if James had made up the story of finding the rabbit. But even if he hadn't, he'd still bought all the gubbins to go with it. The hutch must have cost a pretty penny on its own, and then there was the run, the bowls, the bedding, the food. And not to mention having the creature neutered and vaccinated – vet bills weren't cheap, she knew.

She had to admit, though, that it was certainly more original than taking her out for a slap-up dinner in a posh restaurant. But it was also sneaky – trying to get to her through her son. Despite what Tia had told her, she still wasn't sure about James or his motives. He was certainly going to an awful lot of trouble for a casual fling, but her instincts told her only heartbreak would come of his pursuit of her. He was way out of her league, and she knew it.

Against her better judgement, she allowed Danny to set up the litter tray when they got home, and she then spent an anxious hour following around a quietly exploring Mary and waiting for her to do a whoopsie on the floor.

'See, Mum, she only goes in one corner of her hutch, so James suggested that I put a bit of the hay that she wee-ed and pooped on in the litter tray, so she knows where she'd supposed to go.'

'Did you wash your hands afterwards?'

He nodded. 'James told me I had to wash my hands after I cleaned out the hutch and after I handle her.' He giggled. 'He said it wouldn't be good for Mary to catch my germs. Isn't he silly, Mummy?'

He certainly was, but silly or not, he'd made a very favourable impression on her son.

Edie wasn't entirely sure that was a good thing.

Chapter 14

This was the moment Edie had been dreading ever since Tia had gone behind her mother-in-law's and Mrs C's back: both she and Mrs Carrington had been summoned to The Manor for Tia's dress fitting – the dress which wouldn't see the light of day. Edie felt awful about the deception, but she had no choice other than to attend, not if she didn't want to draw suspicion. As it was, she was convinced that both Mrs C and Julia Ferris must suspect something; how could they not, when Tia hardly glanced at the dress in its protective carrier, which Edie was holding so carefully. Most brides were practically hyperventilating with excitement at the thought of seeing the dress and the progress that was being made, but not this one. Tia was taking disinterest to a whole new level.

Edie helped Tia out of the simple sundress she was wearing, and gently manoeuvred her into the dress, then tried not to let out a gasp when she saw the bride in the nearly-finished article.

It was so plain, so unadventurous, that she felt like crying.

Tia hardly glanced at it, and when Lady Tonbridge suggested that Tia retired to her room to have a good look at her reflection in the full-length mirror, she went with all the enthusiasm of a condemned man going to the gallows.

'Well, don't just stand there, Edie; go with her,' Mrs C instructed, and she hastened to follow Tia out of the room, her eyes peeled in case James happened to be around. Not that she wanted to see him, but it would be rude not to say hello if she bumped into him…

'It's hideous!' Tia hissed as they made their way to what Edie assumed was Tia's bedroom. Edie was surprised to see that it wasn't just a bedroom she was walking into; Tia and William had half of the downstairs of one of the wings. And what a size it was!

There was a generous hallway with a massive living room leading off from it, a kitchen which she caught a glimpse of through an open door beyond, and three more rooms, two of which she could see were bedrooms. Tia wheeled her chair into the one furthest away, and Edie let out a low whistle without meaning to.

'It's nice, isn't it?' Tia said.

'Nice' wasn't the word that had immediately sprung to mind when Edie stepped inside. She wasn't sure what she'd been expecting, but it hadn't been a room the size of her whole little cottage combined, nor the wide double doors leading to a private courtyard with magnificent views of the terraced gardens and the mountain behind.

The bedroom itself was sumptuous, decked out in grey, black and gold, with the occasional white highlight. There were some signs of Tia's disability, like the hoist to help her get out of bed, but other than that, Edie felt as though she'd stepped back in time to a couple of hundred years ago. There was antique furniture everywhere and old paintings on the wall, a large open fireplace, and an impressive tapestry depicting stags, dogs and men above it.

Tia opened a wardrobe door to reveal a full-length mirror and she stared into it, twisting this way and that. 'Yes, I was right,' she declared. 'Hideous.'

The dress wasn't hideous, not at all – it was classy and elegant, and on the right woman it would look stunning. But the right woman wasn't Tia.

It made her appear plain and she seemed to fade into the background in it, whereas even with the silver and grey gown only just about half-sewn, she'd shimmered and glowed, her face lit from within by the magic of the dress.

No wonder Tia didn't want to wear this one, and Edie applauded the girl's decision and her vision. This was a lady who knew exactly what she wanted, and she'd been right.

'I'd better check if it needs any alterations,' Edie said, 'otherwise Mrs Carrington might smell a rat.'

'That wouldn't do,' Tia agreed. 'I want it to be a complete surprise.'

As did Edie. If Mrs C had even an inkling of what was going on, the consequences didn't bear thinking about. She shuddered and glanced over her shoulder nervously, as if she expected Mrs Carrington to be lurking by the door ready to confront her.

After making a few small alterations to the dress, Edie said they were done, but Tia caught hold of her arm and held her back.

'How's the *real* dress coming along?' she whispered.

'Now that you've chosen the fabric, I'm going to go to the wholesaler in Bristol who supplies most of Moira's material, and pick up what's needed. I've got Monday off, and Danny will be in school, so I'll go then. Once I've got the material, it'll take me at least a week to make the dress, and that's without the decorations.'

'Fantastic! I can't wait to see it.'

That reaction was more like it, Edie thought. Tia was behaving more like an excited bride eager for her wedding day, and not like a prisoner who'd just been given an orange jumpsuit. Suddenly Edie was thankful that she'd agreed to make a second dress for her, the dress of her dreams, the dress she deserved.

Edie followed Tia back across the hall towards the drawing room, trying not to look around too much as she slipped her tin of pins back into her work bag.

'He's not here, you know,' Tia said, noticing Edie glancing about.

'Excuse me?'

'James. He's at Hersley Hall but he'll be back later. Do you want me to say you were looking for him?'

Edie was appalled. 'No. Thank you.' Her reply was rather stiff, but she couldn't help it. Was her interest in him that obvious?

She'd have to do something about that, and she tried to make a concerted effort to push him from her mind. The fact that she'd been half hoping she might bump into him was neither here nor there.

Hersley Hall, eh? She'd been there on a school trip once (nearly everyone around these parts did), and it was more of a castle than a house. It was three to four times the size of Tonbridge Manor, for a start, and its grounds were huge. It was owned by one family, who still lived in a part of it, and was open to the public, those rooms having displays ranging from medieval times to Victorian.

She wondered what he was doing there.

Maybe his family owned it, or they were relations of his?

She bet he wasn't delivering the vegetables for dinner or giving them a quote for a spot of plastering. He'd have a much grander reason for hobnobbing with the landed gentry, especially considering he was one of them himself. Whatever the reason, if he was visiting Hersley Hall it only served to convince her that he was far too posh for her.

'There will be another fitting once Edie has completed these minor adjustments,' Mrs C announced when Edie showed her what needed to be done. 'Then there will be a final fitting a week or so before the great day itself. Of course, if you have any concerns, you have my number.'

Edie noticed that Mrs C didn't add her usual admonishment to the bride to be careful not to let her weight fluctuate too much between now and then. In fact, she was being quite obsequious; Edie thought that if she'd had a forelock, she'd be tugging it. As it was, Edie fully expected her to drop a curtsey when the housekeeper was summoned to the drawing room to show them out.

Back at the shop, Edie hastened to begin the minor alterations to the dress, wanting to get them done quickly so she never had to set eyes on it again. The sooner this whole business was over with the better, as far as she was concerned – then she needn't have anything more to do with undercover dresses or handsome men who were too gorgeous and nice for their own good.

Chapter 15

'Thank you,' Edie said, as she climbed into James's car.

'Don't thank me, thank Tia. She was the one who told me you had to take a trip to Bristol. I know you don't have transport of your own, so...' He shrugged.

'I could have caught the train, but it would have been a hell of a journey, so I think I'll stick with thanking you,' she insisted. 'Although haven't you got better things to do than driving me halfway across the country?' Like work, she almost added.

'Not today,' he replied.

She wondered if he did any real work at all, whether he had a proper job, and suspected he didn't. How could he, when he was free on a Monday? Oh, how she would love to be in a position where she didn't have to work her fingers to the bone to keep a roof over her and Danny's heads. Of course, she would still do what she loved – designing and creating beautiful gowns – but she'd be able to pick and choose. She'd have the luxury of allowing her imagination to run riot and—

'Is anything wrong?'

James's question snapped her out of her reverie. Oh dear, had he detected her attempt to keep her distance from him?

'No – why do you ask?' she replied, then wished she hadn't, because she wasn't entirely sure she wanted to hear his answer.

'You seemed a little sad for a moment,' he said.

By now, they were hurtling down the A40 towards the motorway, having shot past Abergavenny, Tanglewood's nearest town.

'Just thinking about work,' she said lightly.

'Do you enjoy your job?'

'Some of it.'

'Which parts?'

'Getting an idea in my head and seeing it come to life. The whole process of creating a dress that no one has designed before, seeing the finished article, and knowing it was all my own work. But more than anything, I love seeing the looks on the faces of the brides when they try their finished dresses on for the first time, and they realise the dress is perfect and that they, too, can be a princess for a day.'

'It's a wonderful thing that you're doing for Tia,' he said quietly. 'It means such a lot to her.'

Edie could tell, and that was the only reason she was doing it. The money would come in handy, she admitted, but the risk of Mrs Carrington finding out was greater than any financial gain. If Lady Tonbridge hadn't insisted on such an inappropriate dress for her future daughter-in-law, then Edie wouldn't have found herself in this position.

'What are the bits you don't like?' he asked.

She paused for a second to gather her thoughts, wondering how honest she could allow herself to be. 'Mrs Carrington,' she said, staring out of the window as James negotiated the roundabout that would take them on the road to Newport and the M4 beyond. Raglan Castle, a ruined medieval monolith, was on their left, complete with towers and battlements: a far cry from the luxury of The Manor.

'What about her?'

'She can be rather difficult to work for.'

'I gathered that,' he said. 'I get the impression that she and Julia are cut from the same cloth.'

'Don't get me wrong,' Edie hastened to say. 'I'm extremely grateful to her for giving me a job. After I had Danny life looked a little bleak for a while. I had to live with my mum, which was hard on her, having a new baby in the house, and although she picks him up from school a couple of days a week and looks after him during the school holidays sometimes, I couldn't expect her to have him full time while I went back to work. She's not that well, and she has her own life to lead.'

'I can see that it would have been tough for all of you. How did you come to work at Moira's?'

'She needed a seamstress because the one she'd been using moved away. I was convenient and cheap, and desperate. I'm also good at it.' Edie added the last in a defiant tone, as if she expected him to refute her claim.

'I'm sure you are,' he said, but she couldn't work out whether his support was genuine or whether he was patronising her; after all, as far as she knew, he hadn't seen any of her work.

'I didn't like the way she treated you,' he said, his eyes firmly on the road as he overtook a huge lorry.

Edie made a face. 'It's just the way she is.'

'Don't take this the wrong way, but I get the impression that she *still* sees you as convenient, cheap and desperate.'

It stung to hear her words quoted back to her, especially since they had a ring of truth, because that was exactly how she suspected Mrs C viewed her. After six years of being in her employ, Edie was no closer to knowing any more about the woman since she'd first started working for her. And she'd not had a pay rise in all that time, either. But beggars couldn't be choosers, and that's what she was.

She ignored James's comment and said, 'It's not that so much. I know she's my employer, but I wish she'd treat me more as an equal. For instance, she pooh-poohed all my suggestions for advertising to bring in new business. She's always operated on a word-of-mouth basis and doesn't see why she should change. I haven't viewed the accounts, but I can tell that clients are gradually dwindling in the six years I've worked there. People tend to go to the internet first, but Moira's doesn't even have a website. I've offered to help set one up, but she's not interested. She doesn't even have a billboard on the street to let passers-by know we're there.' Edie sighed in frustration. 'Moira's could be a little goldmine, if only Mrs C would make the effort.'

'Would you like to manage your own shop one day?'

Would she! That was her dream, a shop of her own. She didn't have Mrs C's innate ability to look at a bride and know exactly the style of dress that would illuminate the woman's best features, but she was learning, and she'd spent enough time sitting in on appointments that she had a fair idea how to judge what might suit someone. She was sure the more practice she had, the better she would become.

Her voice was wistful as she replied, 'One day, I'd love to have my own place, but one day isn't likely to be any time soon. Danny is still so young, and there's the little question of money. It would cost more than I earn in a year to get something like Moira's off the ground.'

That was enough about her. Sometimes she was fed up of thinking about it all. The future seemed so unobtainable and so far away that it was best to concentrate on today and let tomorrow take care of itself.

'Do you work?' she asked him, expecting him to give her a vague answer.

'Of course I do! I have a job in conservation. I currently work for Natural Resources Wales, trying to persuade businesses, farmers and councils to set aside land for wildlife. I'm heading a project called Vestal Verges to try to encourage people to plant the edges of paths, roundabouts and roadsides with wildflowers, instead of cutting them. It might be small fry compared to other projects I've fronted, but it's equally worthwhile.'

Really? Now that did surprise her – not the verges thing, but the fact that he had a job at all. She'd rather expected him to be a Hooray Henry. And even if she had considered that he might have a job, she'd have guessed it to have been in politics or banking.

He sounded incredibly passionate about it, too, and she found it quite endearing. She wasn't heavily into conservation herself, but she could see the necessity of it, and his enthusiasm touched her.

'What other projects?' she asked, and for most of the remainder of the journey, James told her all about his work.

'What made you come back to the UK?' she wanted to know. Tanglewood seemed very tame compared to what he'd been doing.

'The time felt right. All the stuff I was doing is important, but so much work needs to be done here. William had been telling me all about his beavers and how successful the reintroduction had been, and he persuaded me that I could do as much good in Britain, and that my expertise was desperately needed. So I came back about six months ago and bought a smallholding, and here I am.'

A smallholding, eh? Edie bet that hadn't been cheap. Property prices around here were expensive – Tangle-wood might be out in the sticks, but it was a desirable place to live, being in the heart of the Brecon Beacons National Park and delightfully rural. There was a strong farming community, and there's the old adage that you never see a poor farmer. Edie didn't know how true that was, but the fact that James could afford to buy anything bigger than a terraced house in the heart of the village (which was something Edie never saw herself being able to do) only served to reinforce her idea that James was well off. Then there was his connection to the Ferris family, and the fact that he'd been at Hersley Hall.

No, she decided, yet again, this man might be lovely, but they had absolutely nothing in common – their worlds were too far removed from each other for any relationship between the two of them to work.

But it didn't stop her from wishing things were different, despite her vow not to have anything to do with the opposite sex.

Chapter 16

Who knew there were so many different shades of white in the world? James thought as he waited for Edie. He was keeping out of her way and letting her do her thing, trying not to brush up against anything in case he got a smudge of dirt on it. Everything looked so delicate that he was worried about damaging something.

Edie was currently over in a fabric section which was awash with bolts of incredibly fine silver material. The one she was currently examining wouldn't have looked out of place on an Elvish princess (he loved the *Lord of the Rings* series) and he couldn't imagine the amount of work it took to transform the flat length of fabric into something one could wear.

She was in her natural environment, he saw, as she spoke confidently and with knowledge to the sales assistant, who was unrolling metre after metre for her to examine. Edie scrutinised every thread of it; then, only when she was happy with its quality, did she instruct the sales lady to cut her a length off the roll.

He assumed she was done, and he took a step towards the exit in anticipation of being able to escape, but she strolled over to the grey section and went through the whole process again. After that, she moved over to an area in which racks of beads in every conceivable colour were displayed.

It was well over an hour later before she announced she was done, as she staggered towards him, laden with package after carefully wrapped package.

Taking them from her, he checked his watch and noticed that it was lunchtime. His stomach backed him up, rumbling audibly, and she shot him an amused look.

'Shall we take this back to the car, then go and find somewhere for lunch?' he suggested.

Edie nodded, and once her purchases were safely stowed in the back of the vehicle, they headed into the city centre.

'What do you fancy?' He himself would kill for some Italian food, but he'd go with whatever she wanted.

'A Greggs sausage roll will do me,' she said.

'I was thinking of something more substantial.' He saw her face and could have kicked himself. He should have guessed that she probably didn't have the money to throw away on a city-centre restaurant. 'My treat,' he added.

She still looked sceptical.

'Don't worry, it's not a date or anything,' he tried to assure her. 'It's just that I'm starving and haven't had a decent meal since Friday when Julia invited me to join her and Edgar for dinner. I probably wouldn't eat anything except toast and soup if it wasn't for her.'

She nodded, somewhat hesitantly, he thought, but at least she'd not blown him out of the water. It was a step in the right direction, even if she had only accepted because he'd told her it wasn't a date.

And it wasn't. It was two friends enjoying a meal.

Her delight when she walked into the cosy Italian place that he used to frequent many moons ago made having to delay the septic tank guy for another month worthwhile. They found an empty table and examined the menu.

'There's so much to choose from,' she said, and he wondered when the last time she'd been taken out for a meal might have been. From the look on her face, it had been quite some time ago, and he decided to pull out all the stops, no matter how big a dent in his bank account it caused, which was why he ordered a glass of red wine for her, although he stuck to water.

'Tell me,' he said, as they waited for their food to arrive. 'Do you drive?'

'I can, but I don't have a car.' She appeared to be ashamed of it.

'Considering you live within falling-out-of-bed distance of the shop, there probably isn't any point,' he said, hoping to put her at her ease. The thought did occur to him that her lack of transport was most likely a hindrance to her, and he was grateful for being allocated a car by Natural Resources Wales, otherwise he'd be in the same predicament. Having to walk several miles every time he wanted to go into town would be more than a hassle, and would make holding down a job an impossibility. It might very well have come down to a straight choice between buying an old jeep or putting down a deposit on the smallholding. He fully understood her situation.

'Anyway,' he said, 'the fewer vehicles on the road, the better, so you're doing your bit for the environment.'

She took a sip of her wine, not looking convinced, and he didn't blame her. Living in such a rural area made having access to a car almost a necessity.

As they ate, they spoke some more about his job and hers, making polite small talk while devouring their food. He tried not to watch her, but he couldn't help himself. She was so darned cute, even under the aloofness she projected, which he suspected had more to do with shyness than being standoffish. She appeared to be naturally reserved, and even though he'd got to know her a little better, she still reminded him of a wary forest creature ready to flee at the slightest hint of danger.

He sincerely hoped she was starting to become more used to him and less reserved, but he wasn't certain he was making all that much headway with her.

Despite only drinking water, the words were out of his mouth before he had a chance to think about what he was about to say. 'Why do you keep refusing to go out with me? If it's because of Danny, then I fully understand, but I think Danny is a great kid. Bring him along, we can always go somewhere he'd enjoy.'

Her expression was inscrutable, and he wondered for an awful moment if he'd pushed her too far. Perhaps she didn't want to go out with him, and here he was, backing her into a corner, almost forcing her to say yes.

'OK,' she replied, so slowly he was certain that was exactly what he'd done, and he wanted to kick himself. The last thing he intended was to make her feel pressurised into going out with him.

'Look, you don't have to,' he began, but she held up a hand.

'I want to, as long as you're sure you don't mind Danny tagging along.'

'Of course I don't mind. He's the most important thing in your life. Bringing up a child on your own can't be easy. Anyone who wants to get close to you has to understand that and fully accept it.'

She was looking at him with wide eyes, and he hoped he'd said the right thing and not put his foot in it.

'Yes,' she said, 'that's exactly it. We come as a package; you don't get one without the other.'

When he reached across the table and placed his hand on hers to say, 'That's absolutely fine by me,' he could have sworn she felt the startling bolt of electricity between them.

Bloody hell, he was falling for her hard and fast – he just hoped she felt the same way and he wasn't about to get his heart well and truly broken.

Chapter 17

This time, when James came to pick her up, the reason had nothing to do with wedding dresses. They were off out for the day, Danny bouncing around with barely contained excitement.

'Are we going to the stables again?' he asked.

'No, James is taking us to an apiary.'

'Will there be gorillas?'

Oops. She should have explained herself better, and she hoped her son wouldn't be disappointed when he realised what an apiary was. 'It's where bees live,' she explained.

He gave her a doubtful look. 'Bees live in hives,' he said.

'An apiary is where hives are, and where there are several hives in the same place, that's what it's called.' She knew this because she'd looked it up. She hadn't known what an apiary was either, until yesterday.

For a second, Danny seemed crestfallen, but he soon perked up, asking, 'Can I hold a bee?'

'I'm not sure.' Did one hold a bee as such, or did one of the insects simply land on you, and could that be classed as the same thing?

'I want to hold one,' he stated firmly. 'Can you stroke a bee?'

Edie was fairly sure you couldn't, but, then again, she didn't know a great deal about them. 'I wouldn't have thought so,' she said, 'but I bet it'll let you have a little taste of the honey, if you ask it nicely.'

She'd been pleased and a little apprehensive when James had called to suggest the three of them go out for the day, and even more nervous when he'd told her what he had planned. When she'd made it clear over lunch the other day that Danny had to accompany her, and James had said they'd go somewhere he'd enjoy, she'd been expecting a theme park, or something equally flashy and expensive. Viewing beehives was certainly different…

The knock on the door made her jump and she hurried to open it. Seeing him standing there in faded jeans and a white T-shirt, a lock of hair flopping over his brow and a wide grin on his lips, made her heart do a kind of double-thump. But it wasn't her he greeted first, it was Danny, who was hovering behind her.

'How's Mary?' he asked.

Danny grabbed hold of James's hand and dragged him into the little hallway, forcing him to brush up against her, and another spark fizzed through her at the unexpected contact. His eyes flashed to hers, and she knew he'd felt it, too. For the briefest of seconds their gazes held, before James was obliged to follow the force of nature that was her son.

As she collected her bag, a couple of hoodies and her keys, she could hear Danny talking nineteen to the dozen as he told James how well he'd been caring for the rabbit, and how they'd taken her for her first walk, and how he'd persuaded his mum to allow him to bring Mary indoors, although it had only been for an hour or so at a time, and that he wanted her inside because he was especially worried about her getting cold in the winter.

'She's fine outside for the moment,' James replied. 'It's not cold yet, and she's got plenty of bedding. Besides, wild rabbits live outdoors all year round. You don't hear of them knocking at your door and asking to come in for a warm by the fire, do you?'

'You're as silly as my mummy,' Danny said.

Her already fluttery heart almost stopped when James replied, 'Your mummy isn't silly – she's lovely. She's sensible, too, and brave.'

'Brave?' Danny asked, and the doubt in his voice made her smile.

'I've seen her with a dozen sharp pins in her mouth. I call that brave.'

'Oh, that's for her sewing.' Danny didn't sound impressed. Knowing her son, he'd probably been hoping to be told that she fought dragons or had killed a witch.

James was unperturbed. 'Have you seen the size of them? They're huge. I wouldn't put one of those in my mouth.'

'Would you put a bee in your mouth?' Danny wanted to know.

'Probably not, but I have eaten fried grasshoppers.'

Edie shuddered, but Danny was merely curious. 'What did they taste like?'

'Not very nice.'

'How about spiders? Have you eaten one of those?'

The pair of them were still chatting about eating nasty things (Danny's contribution to the conversation was a worm) when they came back inside.

'Mummy, Mummy, James has eaten bugs. Can I try some?'

'I don't think Sainsbury's sells them,' she replied, ushering them outside.

'Aww...'

'If he hands me a pile of woodlice and asks me to cook them, I'll know who to blame,' she hissed at James as she locked her front door.

'I'd try sautéing them in a little butter and garlic,' he laughed, and she gave him a playful tap on the arm.

Then she paused. She was *flirting*, she realised. She didn't think she'd ever flirted in her life before; she didn't think she'd known how to. But here she was, one step away from fluttering her eyelashes and giggling girlishly.

It was actually quite pleasant. Up until now, she'd not seen the attraction, but...

'Right, who wants to see one of the most important creatures on the planet?' James asked, once the three of them were settled in the car and safely strapped in.

Danny's hand shot up. 'Me! Me!'

'Let's go then,' James said, pulling away from the kerb.

Danny tapped her on the shoulder, and she swivelled around to look at him.

'Yes, love?'

His face was a mixture of confusion and accusation. 'You told me we were going to an a-peer-ary.'

'We are.' James spoke for her and she was perfectly happy for him to do the explaining, considering she had no clue what he was on about.

'Do you like strawberries?' James asked.

Danny nodded, but his eyes darted to Edie and she shrugged. The conversation seemed to have gone off at a tangent.

'What about apples?' James asked.

Another nod.

'Peas?'

'Yes, and I like carrots, too.'

'What about tomatoes?'

'Yep.'

'Without bees, there wouldn't be any of those things,' James told him. 'Bees are the main pollinators of many fruit, vegetables, nuts and seeds. Do you know what pollen is?'

'It makes you sneeze, and your eyes run. Ben, in my class, has hay fever.'

'Pollen does much more than give people hay fever,' James said, and for the next few minutes he explained the facts about pollen, before finishing with, 'Don't they get taught this stuff in schools?'

Edie grimaced. 'Apparently not. It seems that many children don't know where their food comes from, which is surprising since Tanglewood is in the heart of a farming community.'

She thought she heard him mutter, 'That's another project for me, then,' but she couldn't be sure.

'OK,' he said, 'now you know what pollen is, what it does, and the part the bees play, you're going to see these insects in action. Did you know that bees can talk to each other?'

He was very good with children, Edie thought, listening to him tell Danny all about waggle dances (who knew?); he was knowledgeable and interesting, and he didn't talk down to Danny, the way some adults did. If he thought Danny didn't understand the terminology being used or the concept, then he simply rephrased it.

'It's not only us humans who'd starve if all the bees disappeared. Animals would suffer, too, because bees pollinate the plants they eat but we don't. And not only that, bees are food for other things, so without them, we'd all go hungry. But there is one more reason why we need to be kind to bees and make sure we don't cut down all the flowers they feed off. Can you guess what it is?'

Danny, wide-eyed and absorbing everything he was being told with complete concentration, shook his head.

'I'll give you a clue,' James said. 'It's golden and sweet and sticky—'

'Honey!'

'You got it in one.'

They reached the apiary in less than half an hour, and as they got out of the car Edie swore she could hear a steady drone of insect wings under the peace and quiet of the countryside.

They were met by an elderly man who introduced himself as Mr Clarke, who gave them a brief talk on how to behave when they approached the hives.

Edie expected Danny to be nervous (she certainly was – she wasn't too keen on flying things) but her son appeared more interested than concerned. Mr Clarke showed them how to suit up, and even found a mini version for Danny, explaining that his bee farm wasn't generally open to the public, but his grandchildren often helped out, so he could borrow one of their suits.

Then he led them to the hives, and the drone Edie had only thought she'd imagined grew louder.

The air was full of insects busily flying to and fro, entering and leaving the hives in their hundreds.

'See how the worker bees return with their pollen sacks full,' Mr Clarke said, pointing out the tiny yellow loads either side of their abdomens. 'They'll unload them, then go out again, and will spend all day foraging.'

Danny was allowed to get up close and personal with the hives, and the beekeeper showed him a comb and how they collected the honey. Even Edie leaned in close when Mr Clarke pointed out the queen, and she was amazed at the difference in size between it and the worker bees.

'Like us,' the man said, 'bees have their jobs to do. Some, most of the ones you see here, are workers, they're the ones who collect the honey; then there are the drones, and their role is to protect the hive; some bees act as nursery assistants, caring for the larvae. But the most important bee is the queen. Without her, the hive wouldn't survive.'

Mr Clarke very kindly spent an hour or more showing them the hives and talking about the life of bees, until eventually Edie saw that Danny was starting to flag; but before she had a chance to say that maybe they'd had enough for one day, James suggested that they visit the shop and purchase some chilled mead, some honey cakes, and maybe even try some honey ice cream.

'Mead is an alcoholic drink made from honey,' James explained as Edie took a sip, 'but Mrs Clarke makes a non-alcoholic version, just for occasions such as these.'

They drank the mead and had an ice cream each, then browsed the shop, James buying some honey cakes, and Edie leaving with a jar of sticky sweetness, which she was looking forward to drizzling on her toast in the morning.

It would be delicious in porridge, too, she guessed, but she'd save that delicacy for when the weather turned cooler.

'I know you aren't too keen on a picnic,' James began, when they returned to the car, 'but it's such a beautiful day, I thought we could eat outdoors down by the river. I know a nice secluded spot where it'll be safe for Danny to paddle. I've brought a couple of towels,' he added, 'just in case you fancy getting your toes wet.'

And that was exactly what she did, after consuming a delicious lunch of tiny sandwiches, bite-sized pasties, and a selection of Peggy's Tea Shoppe's finest cakes, all washed down with lemonade.

Later, when James dropped her and a tired Danny back at the cottage, she realised she'd had a lovely day. With a lovely man.

'I've enjoyed myself,' he said, walking her to her door, Danny trailing slowly behind them, dragging his feet and yawning hugely.

'So did I.'

'Does that mean you'll come out with me again?' he asked.

She nodded, slipping the key into the lock. When she turned to thank him, she caught her breath at the expression in his eyes, and for a second she forgot Danny was there, and hoped he'd kiss her.

She actually thought he might when he stepped closer, and it was enough to send her blood pressure soaring and to make her heart skip a beat.

'Mummy, I'm thirsty,' a little voice piped up, and the mood was broken, so instead of sweeping her off her feet and kissing her soundly, James gave her a hug and a peck on the cheek.

His parting shot as he left was a slow smile and one word. 'Bats.'

Edie couldn't tell whether it was instead of swearing, or whether he was insulting her.

As it turned out, it was neither.

Chapter 18

Leanne Green eyed her reflection in the viewing area mirror and smiled. 'Bloody hell, I'd forgotten what I look like in a dress,' she announced.

Edie thought she looked gorgeous. The champagne shade suited her colouring, setting off her brown hair and creamy skin. Her friend Karen, Stevie's other bridesmaid, also looked fabulous, even though her hair was a deep brown, almost black, and her skin was a darker tone.

They would make beautiful bridesmaids, and Stevie, Edie knew after seeing her for her final fitting, would make a stunning bride. She wasn't here today (a coffee machine emergency, apparently), but she wasn't needed. Everything was under control, even the flowers, Edie gathered, as Karen asked Leanne about them.

'All in hand,' she was saying, as Edie made a final check on the length of the skirt. 'It's going to be a bit of a rush on the morning to get all the bouquets done, but I'll manage.'

'How's the job in London going? Have you started yet?' Karen asked. 'Or are you waiting for *Budding Stars* to be aired?'

Leanne glanced around. 'Shhh, no one is supposed to know.'

Karen laughed. 'You yourself said you can't keep a secret in Tanglewood.'

The florist sighed. 'I expect you've heard,' she said to Edie.

Edie knew exactly what Leanne was talking about. A few months ago, Leanne Green had entered a competition for a new TV show for florists called *Budding Stars*. Rumour had it that she'd done quite well. It had been a bit of a giveaway that Leanne had disappeared off to London every week for several weeks for filming. Edie had also heard that Leanne had accepted a consulting job with a celebrity florist as a result of being on the show. Edie's former schoolmate was doing very well for herself, indeed.

It made Edie feel rather inadequate. She'd dropped out of college to have Danny, and although she had never, for a single heartbeat, regretted her decision, it did make her feel like the poor relation when she saw other people who she went to school with doing so much better than her.

One day, she promised herself, she'd have her own place.

One day…

'We didn't get a chance to chat last time I was in here,' Leanne was saying to her, and Edie blinked.

She had no idea what the pair of them had to chat about.

'It's odd, isn't it, that we live in the same village,' Leanne continued, 'but our paths never cross. Have you been working here long?'

Edie wanted to say that it felt like forever. 'Nearly seven years.'

'Really? Do you like it?'

'I like designing and making dresses. The one you're wearing is one of mine.'

'Wow! You're so talented. I could never make anything like this.'

'Your forte is flowers,' her friend laughed. 'Stevie's is baking. Everyone has a gift.' She turned to Edie. 'When did you discover yours?'

'I've sewn for as long as I can remember,' she said, 'but I only started designing properly when I was pregnant with my son, about nine years ago.'

All that time spent on her own, having dropped out of college and wondering what the hell she was going to do with her life, the only thing that had kept her sane was designing dresses. She'd drawn so many, the designs would keep her going for years. It was a pity she'd not had the money to bring them to life. Most of them were sitting in a drawer at home, but every now and again, she'd push one under Mrs C's nose and sometimes, just sometimes, her employer would like it enough to let her make a sample to display in the shop.

By the time she'd tuned back into the conversation, it had moved on, and the two girls were discussing Leanne's boyfriend Rex, a Scottish guy who'd moved to the village a little while ago.

Then she heard the name James, and her ears pricked up.

'He's a friend of William's,' Leanne said. 'I haven't seen him for years. His parents used to live not too far from here and he went to the same school as William. He's a bit of a dish now. It's a pity you aren't invited to Tia's wedding – I think you'd get on like a house on fire. And,' she said, 'he's single.'

'That's not going to do me any good, is it, however dishy he might be? You forget I live in London, and nothing will ever entice me to move to the back of beyond.'

'Hey, that's my hometown you're talking about,' Leanne exclaimed.

'Each to his own,' Karen said. 'Personally, I like the bright lights of the big city.'

'So did Stevie, but she ended up living here. You could meet a gorgeous bloke and – ow!'

'Sorry,' Edie murmured, horrified that she'd actually jabbed a pin into Leanne. The flare of jealousy that had shot through her at the thought of Karen being set up with James was so unexpected and strong that she hadn't been able to control her reflexes and she'd accidentally managed to shove the pin into the girl's foot.

Mortified, her face red, she lifted her head, to apologise again, but neither bridesmaid was taking any notice of her. Thankfully, they weren't still talking about James, either, because if they had been, she didn't think she'd have been responsible for her actions.

Chapter 19

James put down the hammer and chisel and leant back, easing out the kinks in his spine. Bloody hell, but this was hard work, and dirty, too. Not only did he have to knock off all the old plaster down to the bare brick, but all the debris needed to be shovelled up and taken to the nearest reclamation site for disposal. He'd already made three trips this morning and the back of his jeep was half full again. He looked a sight, too, with his bare chest covered in grey dust and a towel tied around his nose and mouth to try to protect his lungs.

He should wear a proper face mask and a pair of safety goggles, but he'd woken up this morning with an urge to press on with the renovations which couldn't be denied, and he didn't want to waste any time by having to drive to the nearest DIY store, which was well over half an hour away. As he worked, he tried to analyse this unexpected enthusiasm. Not that he hadn't been keen to get started the minute he'd set eyes on the place, but up until now, he'd been content to take things slowly, to take his time doing the place up.

But today, a sense of urgency had assailed him. As soon as he'd woken up, sunlight streaming through the windows, he'd seen the house through fresh eyes.

It was still practically derelict, only just habitable. No one in their right mind would want to live here in the state it was in. The fact that he'd been relatively content to do so up until now set him to wondering why the sudden urgency. He wasn't expecting visitors, and it wasn't as though he had a deadline to meet. He could please himself, and although it would be nice for the renovations to be finished, there was no rush; he'd lived in worse.

But here he was, up to his dirty ankles in rubble, and frantically hacking off more. The old farmhouse was built of local sandstone, and the inside had been rendered with a layer of grey-black stuff (God only knew what that was). On top of that sat ancient plaster which had been painted and papered over many times. He'd stripped the paper off previously, wanting to see the condition of the walls, which hadn't been good, to say the least. It would all have to come off – every room – and the prospect daunted him. It had to be done, though, before the electrician began rewiring. Only then could he nail on fresh boards and get a fella in to give them a skim of fresh plaster. The plumbing still had to be done (although he had managed to cobble together enough funds to sort out the septic tank), and there was also the little problem of installing central heating. Winters here could be harsh, and he had no intention of going into autumn with nothing but a couple of open fireplaces between him and freezing to death.

Once all those hideously expensive jobs were out of the way, then he could think about the nicer things (still hideously expensive, but much more fun), like a new kitchen and an up-to-date bathroom. Maybe he'd persuade Tia to come and have a look, to give her opinion from a woman's point of view. Or ask Edie. Her cottage was lovely: bright and sunny, yet warm and cosy at the same time. Danny might enjoy it here too, he thought. It would give the lad a chance to run about in the great outdoors, without the need to be supervised.

Maybe he'd ask Edie if he could take the boy along when he went to see the man about the goats. He wasn't exactly sure how the goat hire worked – whether he got to pick the goats, or whether they'd arrive as a job lot. Either way, he needed to have a discussion with the man, and soon. Ideally, he'd like the unwanted growth cleared ('eaten' was probably more accurate) before the winter set in. The pigs could do their work in the spring, and their droppings would serve as a natural fertiliser. The rest of the groundwork would be down to him and sheer hard graft in turning the soil over. He'd be lucky if he managed to plant so much as a potato by next April.

As he picked up his tools once again, he wondered what he was doing in assuming that Edie and Danny would be around come the autumn. He'd only taken her out once, and here he was, building a whole life for himself with the pair of them in it. One date doth not a relationship make, he misquoted to himself. Although he did think it had gone rather well. Danny had definitely enjoyed himself, and the boy had learnt something too. As for Edie, she'd been more restrained, but she'd seemed to have had fun down at the river, and had even got her feet wet.

It was when he was dropping her at home that things had started to get a little more intense, and he didn't know whether she'd have welcomed the kiss he'd been about to give her or not, because Danny, bless him, had spoilt the moment. Maybe that was a good thing – he didn't want to move too fast and scare his little doe off, although he would have loved nothing more than to have taken her in his arms and kissed her until the pair of them were breathless.

He was rather annoyed with himself that he couldn't stop thinking about Edie, so he set to work with gusto, trying to use physical activity to drive her from his mind. But it was no use. She hovered there, a beautiful backdrop to everything he did and thought, until eventually he downed tools and went for a shower. Or what passed for a shower in his neck of the woods, because in the absence of one, he'd rigged up a bucket attached to a length of hose with a common sprinkler head stuck to it and had hung it over the bath. He could have taken the edge off the freezing water by warming a couple of kettles on the ancient range, but he had the feeling a cold shower might do wonders for his equilibrium.

It didn't.

And neither did a two-and-a-half-hour meeting with the National Farmers' Union, because he was still thinking about her when he returned to his car and loosened his tie.

Unable to help himself, he detoured into Tanglewood village, trying to find an excuse to pop into Moira's, just to see Edie's face.

It was no use; he couldn't think of a single reason to visit her at work. So instead, he decided to waste the time between now and when Moira's closed for the day by spending it in Peggy's Tea Shoppe.

It wasn't a total waste, because he could do with refuelling, not having had any lunch, and whatever he ate in here would have to do him for his evening meal, too, because there was very little to eat back at his house.

Stevie, the tea shop owner, gave him a wide smile. 'What can I get you?' she asked, and he took a moment to read the day's specials on the board.

'The ploughman's lunch sounds lovely,' he said. 'Could I have an extra bread roll to go with it?'

'Crikey mate, you're looking smart,' a voice said, and James turned around to see a familiar face.

He'd only known Rex McMillan since he'd come back to the UK, but he'd already had some dealings with the guy, which wasn't surprising considering they were in a similar line of business.

'Why don't you join me?' Rex suggested, taking his rucksack off a chair. 'I've only just ordered, too.'

Grateful not to be alone with his thoughts, James took a seat. Even though he'd lived near Tanglewood all his life, he didn't know many people in the village, so it was nice to make a new friend. Rex had only recently joined the community, having come from Scotland to work for the Beacons National Park as a ranger, so he and James had a lot in common, they'd discovered.

Rex's border collie, Nell, was sitting quietly under the table gazing up adoringly at her master in the hope that he'd feed her the occasional titbit, and Rex duly obliged. James also found himself sneaking her the odd piece of cheese, which she took from him with the delicacy of a surgeon performing an intricate operation. Sometimes he wished he had a dog, but he didn't have the time, and with his house looking like a building site, it probably wouldn't be safe.

'I wonder if you can get hard hats for dogs?' he mused out loud, and Rex sent him a curious glance. 'Sorry, I didn't mean to actually say that aloud,' he said. 'I was just thinking about dogs and building sites.'

Rex didn't seem any the wiser, and James couldn't blame him.

'I've bought the old Hopkins place,' he explained. 'It needs a lot of work.'

'It sure does,' Rex agreed. 'But I'm glad to see it's not being allowed to go to rack and ruin. How much land have you got?'

'A couple of acres. It used to be quite a substantial farm, but I guess parcels of it must have been sold off down the years. It's enough for me, though. A decent vegetable plot and an orchard are all I need, plus a couple of hens, and maybe a goat...'

'No dog?'

'Not yet, but I hope to have one, one day.' An image of an excited Danny being introduced to his very own puppy popped into his mind, and he shooed it away. He was getting ahead of himself as far as Edie and her son were concerned.

He and Rex chatted for a while longer until James realised the time. It was nearly four o'clock and Moira's would be closing soon. He guessed that Edie would probably pick Danny up first and he wanted to be there when she got home.

'Must dash,' he said, calling for the bill.

An elderly lady brought it over.

'Can I have mine, too?' Rex asked. 'I'm meeting Leanne in a minute.' He smiled. 'We're off to the solicitors.'

'You can't be divorcing already – you ain't married,' the old woman said.

Rex chuckled. 'Have you had the pleasure of meeting Betty yet?' he asked James.

'No, he hasn't, but I know who you are, my lad,' Betty said, staring at him. 'You're the bloke who has got little Edie Adams all in a flutter.'

'I am?' James didn't know what else to say.

'You are. Not that she properly believes it yet, but she will.'

Rex chuckled. 'I won't say that Betty is psychic, but she's pretty darned close. You'd better listen to her.' He waited until the old lady had retreated before he said, 'I don't think I've met Edie Adams.'

'She works at Moira's, the wedding shop in the court-yard.'

'Ah, that explains it. I've not had any reason to go in there. Yet.'

'Yet?'

'I'm going to ask Leanne to marry me – but keep it under your hat. I want it to be a surprise. I'm going to pop the question once we get the deeds to the house.'

'Hence the visit to the solicitor?' James guessed.

'That's right; we're currently in the process of buying the house we're renting.'

Rex looked so happy, James was envious. As he settled his bill, all he could think about was that weddings had suddenly become a very important part of his life – and it was all down to a certain pretty seamstress.

His final thought before he went to find her was to wonder what she'd look like in one of her own creations.

Chapter 20

James didn't have to wait long. Within a few minutes of him loitering around in the courtyard, he heard her quick footsteps echoing under the archway, accompanied by the even quicker patter of her son's. Darn it, but the boy was cute, James thought as the two of them came into view. He had his mother's fair hair and blue eyes, and idly James wondered where the child's father was. One day, he hoped Edie would trust him enough to share her story with him. But for now, it was enough to know that the man wasn't on the scene. James was probably being premature, but he didn't want anyone coming between him and his budding relationship with Edie and Danny. He knew he was being selfish, but he couldn't help it. He wanted her – *them* – all to himself.

He pushed away from the wall and walked forward to greet her, registering the surprise on her face. He hoped he was a good surprise and not an unwelcome one. Her smile told him what he needed to know, but underneath it the wariness still lurked.

'Is anything wrong?' she asked.

'Far from it.' He held out his arms and after a slight hesitation, she stepped into them, and allowed him to give her a hug. 'I just wanted to see you, that's all,' he said.

When she pulled away, he could tell that she wasn't sure what to make of that, but all she said was, 'Fancy a cuppa?'

He did. If it allowed him to be with her for longer, he'd happily drink poison.

She led him inside, dumped her bag and Danny's on the floor in the kitchen and filled the kettle. Danny, as James guessed, wanted to show him Mary, so he cheerfully went outside and spent a few minutes admiring the bunny. Danny appeared to be taking excellent care of her, and James heaped praise on the boy.

He left Danny telling Mary all about his day and went back inside to find Edie. She had a cup of tea waiting for him and was busy chopping vegetables.

'Chicken fajitas tonight,' she informed him and, despite his ploughman's earlier, his mouth watered.

'Sounds lovely,' he said, thinking of the packet of three-day-old ham in the fridge and the peas that had been in the freezer for months: not a particularly inspiring combination.

'You can join us, if you like,' she offered. 'There's plenty to go round. But I warn you, the price will be endless rabbit talk and reading Danny a bedtime story. He gets sick of my voice.'

James couldn't imagine such a thing.

'I've not had much practice at reading bedtime stories,' he admitted, 'but how hard can it be?'

She chuckled, and it sent a ripple through him. 'He'll play havoc if you don't put on the voices,' she told him, 'so good luck with that.'

Dinner would be a while yet, so once Edie had finished preparing it, they took their drinks outside into the little yard, and watched Danny playing with the rabbit. It was a proper little suntrap, he discovered, lifting his face to the late afternoon warmth and soaking up the rays. For a man who was so heavily into conservation, he actually spent an inordinate amount of time indoors, usually attending endless meetings or making presentations. Still, at least he was making slow but steady progress, and more and more people were coming to understand that their own actions had consequences for the environment. Only today, he'd managed to persuade the NFU to lobby for even greater subsidies to those farmers who turned their fields over to nature. It seemed silly to pay farmers not to farm, but the way things were going, current farming methods were quickly becoming unsustainable.

'A penny for them?' Edie said, cutting into his thoughts.

'Sorry, I was thinking about the environment, and what we can all do to help.'

'I told everyone in school about the importance of bees,' Danny said, looking up from grooming Mary. 'Miss Harding said she'd ask Mr Ryedale about sowing wild-flowers on the grassy bits beside the paths. We're not allowed to walk on them anyway.' He sounded quite put out by it.

'That's a great idea,' James said. 'Well done, you.'

Danny's little chest puffed out at the praise.

'Shall I see if I can get a seed company to donate some seeds?' James suggested. 'Then it won't cost the school anything.'

'I'll ask Miss Harding,' Danny said. 'She's my teacher and she's lovely.'

'Mr Ryedale is the head teacher,' Edie added by way of an explanation. 'How can *we* help?' she wanted to know. 'I'd like Danny and me to do our bit.'

'You've already helped by taking in a homeless rabbit,' he said. 'She'd probably be an ex-rabbit by now if it wasn't for you and Danny.'

Aw, Edie looked really cute when she blushed, he thought.

'It was a very nice thing you did,' she said. 'I know I wasn't keen at the time but having a pet has been so good for Danny. Thank you.'

'To be honest, you were doing me a favour. I didn't have a clue what I was going to do with her if you hadn't agreed to adopt her.'

They smiled at each other, and James felt his heart melt. God, she was lovely, and she was so unaware of just how adorable she was. It was an irresistible combination, and it made his head swim. There was something about her independence and courage that made him want to protect her. Then he almost laughed out loud at the cliché. Did he really think he was her knight in shining armour and she was a damsel in distress? Because, from where he was sitting, she was managing perfectly well on her own. What he hoped was that even though she didn't *need* him in her life, she might grow to *want* him in it.

James felt remarkably at home and surprisingly domesticated as he helped Danny lay the table, which was usually the boy's job and one which he quite happily relinquished; then he dried the dishes after their meal, while Edie washed.

Danny was allowed an hour or so of downtime watching TV while the grown-ups chatted, then it was time for the child's bath.

'Aw, can't I stay up a bit later?' Danny pleaded.

'You know the rules. Eight o'clock on a school night.'

'It's only seven,' Danny pointed out.

'You always have a bath at seven, then a story,' his mother replied. 'It takes an hour to get you settled.'

James had to bite his lip to stop himself from smiling when Danny pouted and said, 'It's not fair. You get to stay up to talk to him.' He pointed at James.

'That's because I'm a grown-up,' she said, ushering her son out of the room, towards the stairs and the horrors of bath time. 'I don't have to go to bed at eight,' he heard her say.

'Deffo not fair.'

'James will read you a story,' she added, and Danny's happy 'Yay!' floated into the living room.

I could get used to this, James thought, feeling far more relaxed and contented than he'd done for a long time. Some of it he put down to sitting on a decent sofa. Julia's sofas didn't count because they were mostly hard, stuffy antiques that he was scared to sit on anyway in case he marked or damaged them.

Although Edie's home was spotlessly clean and immaculately tidy, it had a lived-in air which made him feel instantly at home. Or that's what he tried to tell himself. The alternative reason, that it was Edie who he felt at home with and not her house, was a concept he'd have to come to terms with. This was all moving incredibly fast and he wasn't sure how he felt about it, or how to act. It was virgin territory, and he felt all the apprehension that was to be expected when heading into the unknown. He just hoped he would come out of it unscathed, although he had a suspicion it was already too late for that.

Storytime was a hilarious affair. It soon became clear that Danny had chosen a favourite book, and one he knew well. James found he had his work cut out to make every character's voice sound unique, and he ended up resorting to acting out the story as well as narrating it, much to Danny's squealing delight.

When he eventually made his way back downstairs, he was exhausted.

'I did warn you,' she said, handing him a glass of something tall and cold. 'Lemon cordial,' she informed him. He had hoped for something a bit stronger, even if it did mean having to walk all the way home.

'I hope Danny hasn't put you off having kids,' she laughed.

'Never! I love kids, and Danny's fantastic. I just didn't expect him to be so… lively.'

'You ain't seen nothing yet. You wait until he has a tantrum. They're rare, admittedly, but they do still happen.'

Does that mean I'm going to be around long enough to witness one? James wondered, fervently hoping that was the case.

'I'm not sure *I* do,' Edie said, breaking into his thoughts.

'Excuse me?'

'Want any more children. I had Danny so young that now he's getting older, I think I might want some time for me.'

That was understandable. At least he'd had plenty of time for himself. 'How old were you?' he asked.

'Eighteen. Obviously, it wasn't planned.' Her smile was small and tight. 'Don't get me wrong, Danny is my whole world, but when you haven't known anything else, you sometimes wonder what things could have been like. I see people my own age, girls I used to know from school, like Leanne Green, making a life for themselves, running their own businesses—'

He stopped her right there by drawing her to him. Surprised, she stopped talking, giving him a doe-eyed, liquid stare instead.

'You listen to me, Edie Adams,' he said. 'You've done something incredible – you've made a new life. Danny is a wonderful, happy, bright, confident boy. Don't you dare put yourself down because you chose to have him. Everyone walks their own path, and your time to shine will come.' He stopped and blinked. 'Wow. That was heavy. But I still mean it.'

Edie said nothing, but continued to stare at him. So he did the only other thing he could think of – he kissed her.

Slowly, he bent his head towards hers, half expecting her to push him away, but when she lifted her chin slightly and her lips parted, he was lost.

Gently, his mouth brushed against hers, lightly, like a butterfly wing. Her lips were so soft, so edible – he wanted to eat her all up. Gradually, he pulled her closer, wrapping his arms around her delicate fragility, totally and utterly lost in her and the sensations flooding through him. He'd never felt so connected to anyone, and desire coursed along every nerve, inundating every cell, until his mind and senses reeled.

'Oh my,' she said, breathlessly, when they eventually came up for air.

'Oh, my,' he echoed.

Oh, my…

Chapter 21

Bats, Edie discovered a couple of evenings later, hadn't been an insult or a description. They were small flying mammals who were cuter than they had any right to be, given their bad press. She was currently holding an extremely tiny pipistrelle. It fitted easily into the palm of her gloved hand (gloves were essential for handling bats, they'd been informed) and a young woman was telling her and Danny, who was studiously holding his own bat with the utmost care and concentration, that the tiny mammals weighed between three and eight grammes and could fit into a matchbox.

'Anyone can become a bat carer with a bit of training,' the girl said, but when Danny gave Edie a hopeful look, she shook her head. A rabbit was one thing, but she didn't think her landlord would be too pleased if she had a houseful of bats, protected species or not.

She looked behind her, giving James a huge smile. As far as second dates went this was a brilliant one. She honestly hadn't thought she'd like bats as much as she did. They were fascinating little creatures.

When he'd told her where he was taking them, she had to admit she'd not been overly keen on the idea, although needless to say Danny had been ecstatic. As far as he was concerned, James was the best thing since sliced bread. Edie was gradually beginning to think the same thing.

'James! James!' Danny was trying not to jump about in excitement, as he was still holding his bat. 'She just said that a single pipistrelle can eat up to three thousand insects a night.'

'See, that's why we need plenty of places for insects to live, otherwise there won't be anything for these little things to eat,' James told him.

Danny's eyes grew wide as Bat Girl explained how echolocation worked, and that the bats only came out at night.

'Is that why we didn't come here in the daytime?' Danny asked.

'We try to keep them as happy as possible,' Bat Girl said. 'They don't like daylight and we don't want to upset them, especially since most of the bats in the rescue centre aren't very well. Our job is to make them better. And once we do, we can release them back into the wild.'

'What was wrong with mine?' Danny brought his face close to the bat, studying it intently.

'We think she got caught up in some fencing, because she came in with a torn wing. It's all better now, though, so we'll give her a final check over then release her close to where she was found.'

Next, Bat Girl took them to the infirmary to show them some of the bats who were in various stages of recovery, but there was an area of the rescue centre that was off-limits because the patients were too ill for visitors.

'Is it too late to grab a quick bar snack?' James asked after they'd thanked the staff at the bat rescue centre and were heading back to the car.

Edie did a rapid mental review of her finances. James might be well off, but she had no intention of letting him pay for her and Danny every time they went out.

'Only if you let me pay this time,' she said, watching his face, but he didn't give any indication that he was embarrassed or put out by her offer.

'OK,' he said after a while, 'but I was only thinking of a pub I know around the corner. They do fantastic scampi and chips, good portions, and a reasonable price, too.'

All Edie could hope was that his idea of reasonable was somewhere near hers.

Thankfully, it was, she saw, as they walked into a small, out-of-the-way pub with a small, inexpensive menu. Even with it being on the cheap side, Edie knew she'd have to get creative with their meals for the rest of the week. Crikey, but this dating business was more expensive than she remembered it being. Saying that, the last time she'd dated anyone had been when she was in college, and her boyfriend (Danny's father) had been as skint as she'd been; a meal out had consisted of a burger meal from McDonald's. In fact, it was just after one of those that she'd gotten carried away in the back seat of his decrepit Fiesta. Danny had been the result, and although she'd berated herself over the years for being so stupid, she wouldn't have done anything differently if it meant she didn't have Danny in her life.

She hoped James didn't notice that she chose the least expensive thing on the menu – which happened to be the scampi and chips – and to her relief he chose the same. Danny had a children's meal, and the three of them settled back with their drinks.

'So then, is Mary in training yet?' James asked Danny. 'I noticed there's rabbit racing in the Tanglewood Summer Fete.'

Danny's face lit up. 'Can Mary race, Mum?'

'What does it entail? They had sheep racing last year – will it be like that?' Edie asked.

'I expect so,' James said.

'But who'll ride her? I'm too big,' Danny wailed.

James chuckled. 'They don't have jockeys. Someone lets the rabbit go at one end of the track, while another person stands at the end with a treat.'

'I can do that, can't I, Mummy? She likes chocolate buttons.' He clapped a hand to his mouth. 'Oops.'

'She shouldn't be eating human food,' Edie scolded. 'It's not good for her.'

Danny's response made her smile. 'She eats carrots and I eat carrots, too. You make me.'

'But you like carrots.'

'I like chocolate buttons better.'

Edie sent James a helpless look. He shrugged, but she could tell he was trying not to laugh.

'Danny,' she said, aiming for stern and not succeeding. 'Only feed her the things James has said she can eat. You don't want her to get ill, do you?'

He looked horrified at the idea, and she hoped it was enough to discourage him from feeding any more chocolate to the poor rabbit. 'But how will I get her to come to me?' he asked.

James had the answer to that one. 'The best way to train her is to not feed her in the morning, then she'll be super hungry and should come running to you when she sees you have some food,' he suggested.

'I didn't know you were such an expert on rabbit training,' Edie laughed.

James leant close and whispered, 'Shhh, don't tell Danny, but I'm not.'

Danny was all ears. 'Not what?'

'Never you mind,' she said to him.

'Ew, are you talking about kissing?'

'No, we are not!' she exclaimed. But after James had taken them home, Danny having to be carried because it was way past his bedtime and he was exhausted, James did more than just talk about kissing.

With Danny safely tucked up in bed sound asleep, James patted the sofa and Edie sank down next to him with a contented sigh.

'Thank you for this evening,' she said. 'Danny loved it.'

'Just Danny?'

'OK, I admit it, the bats were cute.'

'Not as cute as you,' he replied, snaking an arm around her and pulling her close.

She snuggled into him. It felt so right being in his arms, as though it was meant to be.

He twisted slightly to face her, and she knew he was going to kiss her again.

This was becoming a habit, and not one she wanted to break. His lips fluttered against hers, softly at first, becoming bolder as she melted into him, her own lips parting in response.

When they finally broke apart, she saw the hunger in his eyes and her heart did a slow flip-flop. She never thought she'd ever let herself fall for another man again, but she knew she was in over her head with James, and the experience was utterly delightful. But, she vowed, she wanted to take it slow, to make certain that what she was doing was right for her, and for Danny. It helped that Danny adored him, and James seemed to genuinely like him in return.

She wasn't sure whether she was relieved or disappointed when, with a kiss on the end of her nose, James released her and stood up.

'I'd better be off,' he said. 'I've got a meeting with the Butterfly Association in the morning and I need to be on top form.'

Edie was sorry to see him go, but grateful that he'd decided to leave before she'd have been forced to have the it's-too-soon conversation with him.

Unfortunately, unlike her son, she was too wired to sleep, so she retreated to the little table in the corner of her room where her sewing machine sat, and worked on Tia's dress until she was too exhausted to see straight. As she stumbled up to bed, her last thought was of James, and the effect he was having on her once predictable and safe life.

Chapter 22

The last thing Edie wanted to do the following day when she got in from work was to take Danny and Mary for a walk. Or should she say a training session, because Danny was adamant that he wanted to enter Mary into the rabbit race on the weekend, and he was determined to give his bunny the best chance of winning.

'OK,' she gave in. 'But homework first.' At Danny's age, he didn't have a lot, but Edie wanted to instil in him the good practice of getting homework out of the way as soon as he came home, before he started high school and was given loads of it, although that big event was a couple of years away yet. Reluctantly, he got out his literacy book and set to, but very soon she found she was roped in to help.

Eventually, he'd completed what he needed to do for his teacher and was now raring to go, with a rather excited Mary hopping about on the end of the lead. As usual, Edie carried the rabbit until they reached the big field by the river, at which point she placed Mary gently on the ground and allowed her to explore a little before they started her training. The afternoon was warm and sunny, and the scent of the river and recently mown grass hung on the air. A faint breeze ruffled her hair and she was glad she was outside. Although she had a tonne of sewing to do, it would have been a waste to pass this up.

A wide path had been mown into the meadow and trampled by numerous walkers, both with and without dogs, but the rest of the field remained untouched; the soft wind sighed through the long grass and delicate blooms of wildflowers dotted the field. The hum of insects ebbed and flowed as the little creatures went about their business, and every so often Edie batted away one of them when it came too close. The field was also alive with butterflies, and for a little while she and Danny tried to count them, giggling like fools when they failed to get their results to tally again and again.

'Pesky critters,' Danny chortled, and Edie wondered where he'd got the expression from. James, maybe? He had certainly given her son an appreciation of wildlife, and she was grateful for it. In a subtle way, James was teaching him science, too, she realised, thinking back to his explanation about flowers and pollination, and about bats and their sonar.

Damn it, there she was, thinking about James again. Was she ever going to get this man out of her head? Did she even want to?

It was only when she and Danny began the training session (although how effective training a rabbit could be, Edie had yet to fathom) that she realised she'd have to let Mary off the lead. At just over three feet, the length of soft leather was nowhere near long enough to allow Mary a proper run. In two hops she'd reached Danny and the little chunk of carrot he was holding out to her. The rabbit ate it eagerly, then looked for more.

She made a decision. 'We're going to have to let her off.'

Danny looked worried. 'What if she runs away?

'She won't. She's too interested in the carrots.'

Mary was standing on her hind legs, pawing at his hands, her nose twitching. Edie picked her up and told Danny to stay where he was.

'Get some carrot ready,' she called over her shoulder.

'Don't go too far,' he warned.

'I won't.' She halted about ten feet away, and placed Mary on the grass.

The bunny was only just visible in the long, waving stalks, but there was a flattish trail where Edie had trodden it down, leading back to Danny.

'Call her,' Edie said, letting go of the rabbit.

'Mary, Mary, look, carrot,' Danny cooed, and the rabbit took a slow, hesitant hop towards him. He crouched down, holding out his hand with the little chunk of carrot visible on his palm.

'Mary, come here Mary, carrot,' he called.

The rabbit risked another hop, then another, each one slightly faster than the first, then made a final mad dash to claim her reward.

'There's a good girl. Well done, Mary,' he said to her, then looked at his mother. 'She knows her name.'

Edie thought that the only thing the rabbit knew was that he had carrots, but she didn't disillusion him. She walked slowly back to her son and picked Mary up again. The rabbit nestled into her arms, perfectly happy, and Edie bent her head to nuzzle the soft, sweet-smelling fur, before putting her back on the ground.

After she'd put Mary down, Danny called his pet to him once more. This time the rabbit's progress was slightly faster; she was getting the hang of it. The bunny looked quite sweet hopping away from her, her little tail up, her long back legs lolloping. The pair of them tried twice more, until Mary was fairly galloping from Edie to Danny, the allure of fresh, crunchy carrot chunks proving irresistible to the hungry little animal.

Finally, Edie decided that Mary had probably had enough. They would come out with her tomorrow, weather permitting, and try again, from a slightly increased distance, because she wasn't sure how long this rabbit racing course was, and she decided she needed to find out. Then she shook her head, laughing silently at herself. If anyone had told her that she'd be training a rabbit to go racing, she'd have suggested that they needed to visit a doctor.

Yet here she was, standing in a field with a snow-white bunny who was wearing a little red harness, and thinking it was a perfectly normal thing to do. Not only that, but she'd been on two weird dates (if you could call them dates, considering she'd taken her son along) and had kissed a man, twice. She must be going barmy—

Oh!

'Mary! *No!*' she cried as Mary, who had been sitting on her haunches, her paws grasping a piece of carrot, abruptly dropped the treat, and shot off into the long grass.

Danny was frozen to the spot, horror evident in his wide eyes and open mouth. Edie hadn't even managed to take one step in the rabbit's general direction when two huge dogs charged into view, their jaws open, their ears flapping, as they shot past Danny and dived into the grass, in hot pursuit of the rabbit.

'Mary!' Danny squealed at the top of his voice, and dashed after the dogs.

Galvanised into action, Edie began to run. Immediately ahead of her was Danny, and in front of him she could see the dogs, bounding through the meadow, their ears flapping, tails held high. There was no sign of Mary, not even a ripple in the grass to indicate where she was. But the dogs were still haring about, jigging this way and that, so Edie knew that they hadn't caught her yet.

'Danny, stop!' she yelled, hoping he'd listen. She dreaded to think what would happen if one of the manic dogs decided to target her son instead of the rabbit.

Heart pounding and mouth open wide as she gasped for air, she sprinted across the meadow, hot on the heels of a rabbit, two dogs and a small boy.

Mary was heading for the trees and the hedgerow at the edge of the field, although she wasn't moving in a straight line, if the dogs' kinking and weaving was anything to go by. Edie guessed the rabbit was trying to lose them.

Her breath rasping in her throat and her lungs burning, she became aware she wasn't alone. Someone was running after *her*. Sudden fear shot through her, dumping a load of adrenalin into her beleaguered legs and giving her an added burst of speed.

Legs and arms pumping, she dashed through the grass, not feeling the sting and whip of nettles, nor the prick and snag of thistles as she careened past.

The sound of someone close behind her grew louder, and she let out a breathless scream as she caught sight of a figure out of the corner of her eye before a largish man, whose red face was slick with sweat, lumbered past her.

'Carlos, Rita,' he wheezed. 'Come here.' The last word ended in a type of gasping cough.

Then she heard a child's high-pitched scream, and she knew instinctively it came from her son.

'Danny!' she yelled. 'I'm coming.'

'Mummy, Mummy, get them off me.'

Oh. My. God. The dogs were attacking her son—

Then she saw him, sprawled in the grass, the two dogs all over him.

'Get those things off him,' she screeched, diving on top of the nearest one, regardless of her own safety. She grabbed the mutt around the back end and wrestled it away from her child. But before she could register what was happening, the dog had squirmed around until it was on top of her, jaws agape, eyes wild.

She steeled herself to feel the slash of savage jaws in her flesh, raising her hands to fend it off. As she did so, a hot wet tongue slid across her face, and she simply knew she was going to have her throat torn out.

The dog slobbered again, wetting her face with its enormous tongue.

'Rita, leave her alone,' the man gasped, and suddenly the ravening beast's weight lifted off her as the man dragged it away.

'Danny,' she cried, rolling over, and getting onto all fours and crawling towards him, prepared to kill the wolf who was savaging her son.

She stopped.

Danny wasn't being mauled to death.

He was being licked to death instead, by a large white and black spotted dog, with the most ridiculously long tongue.

Danny was trying to fend it off, but was giggling too much for his efforts to be all that effective.

'Carlos, come here, boy,' the man wheezed, and the dog obediently left Danny and trotted to his master's side, where he promptly sat, staring at the man adoringly. 'Sorry about that,' the dog's owner said. 'They're a couple of softies, but I can see why you were frightened. I would have been too, if I didn't know them.' He bent down and clipped a leash on each dog, who were now acting as though butter wouldn't melt in their lolling-tongued jaws.

'I've no idea what made them run off like that,' the bloke said.

'I do.' Edie scrambled to her feet and helped Danny up.

Her son was no longer giggling; he now looked close to tears.

'A rabbit,' she said.

'Oh, that would explain it. They're always chasing rabbits, but they've never caught one yet. It's a bit early in the evening for rabbits to be out and about, though. They usually prefer to be out at dusk.'

'It's not a wild rabbit,' Edie began, but Danny interrupted her.

'She's my rabbit, and her name is Mary, and your dogs scared her and now she's run away.' The last came out as a sob.

Edie put her hand on his shoulder. 'She won't have gone far,' she said, praying it was true, but not for a minute believing it was. Mary could be halfway up the nearest mountain by now.

'Oh, I see,' the man said, not seeing at all.

'We were taking it for a walk,' Edie explained, 'and we'd let her off her lead because we're training her for the rabbit race at the Summer Fete.'

The poor fellow looked even more bewildered, and Edie felt quite sorry for him. But not as sorry as she felt for Danny. The child was heartbroken.

'We'd better start looking for her,' Edie said. 'Danny, you call her because she's used to coming to you. Have you got any carrot left?'

His hand went to his pocket and he nodded.

'Would you like some help?' the man offered.

'That's very kind of you, but I think your dogs might scare her even more.'

'Are you Mr Disney?' Danny asked, momentarily distracted by the dogs, as they rose to a standing position in unison.

Edie knew immediately what he was referring to.

'No, Dan, he just owns the same kind of dogs, that's all. *One Hundred and One Dalmatians*,' she said to the man.

'Ah, ha ha. No, I'm not Walt Disney. I wish I was; I could do with some of his money. Right, I'd better be off then. Good luck with finding the rabbit.'

Thanks, Edie thought, waiting until he and his dogs were at a safe distance before she began the search. She and Danny were going to need it.

Chapter 23

Encroaching darkness forced Edie to give up the search, despite Danny's pleading. He was so tired he could hardly put one foot in front of the other; he was also filthy, covered in little scratches, and he hadn't eaten since lunch. She knew he wasn't capable of carrying on for much longer, and they still had a bit of a walk until they made it home.

Unless a miracle happened, Edie would have to accept that the rabbit was gone for good. Maybe, if Mary was lucky, some other kindly soul would find her and take her in.

'Please, Mum!' he begged, his voice hoarse from shouting.

She looked at his tear-stained face, smeared with dirt, his eyes red and swollen, and her heart went out to him. But she couldn't in all conscience allow him to search for his pet any longer.

'Mary's gone, poppet,' she said.

'But she'll be back, won't she?' His voice broke and he sobbed again.

Edie wanted to sob with him, but she had to stay strong for his sake. She'd cry later, in bed, when he couldn't hear her, but her tears would be more for him than for Mary; however cute the rabbit was, her priority was her son, and right now she needed to get him home, feed him, bathe him, and put him to bed.

'I bet James can find her,' he said for about the hundredth time.

'I've tried calling him, Dan, but he's not answering his phone,' she said. 'I'll tell him all about Mary as soon as I get hold of him.'

Danny was fast asleep and she was on the verge of nodding off, sitting in the chair with an unwatched period drama playing on the TV in the background, her thoughts very much with Danny and his palpable distress, when James finally called.

'What's wrong?' he asked. 'I've had several missed calls from you. Is it Danny?'

'Danny's fine. It's Mary,' she said, and she proceeded to tell him what happened.

'I'll go down to the river,' he said.

Although grateful for the offer, Edie knew it was useless. Mary could be anywhere by now, and the odds of James finding her were slim, to say the least.

'It's hopeless,' she told him. 'You'll be wasting your time.'

'Not necessarily. Rabbits usually come out late at night and in the early morning. She could have taken refuge in a burrow and is waiting until she knows it's safe to come out. If other rabbits are above ground, then she might be, too. Please, I want to do this.' Then he added, 'If I hadn't given Danny the rabbit, or if I hadn't mentioned the rabbit race...' He trailed off.

'OK,' she agreed, knowing she couldn't prevent him from searching for Mary if he wanted to; she was grateful for his concern. Danny would certainly appreciate James's effort, even if it did turn out to be futile.

She was just about to go to bed when she heard a soft tap on the door. Instantly awake and fearing bad news, she hurried to open it. As she thought, it was James: a very tired, rather grubby, but extremely jubilant James.

He was holding Mary in his arms, cuddling her into his chest as though he'd never let her go.

'You found her!' she exclaimed, trying to keep her voice down for fear of waking Danny.

'Not exactly. She found me, or to be exact, she found you and Danny. I was popping back to your house to see if there was any news, and there she was, sitting on the doorstep as large as life.'

'Oh, bless her,' Edie cried, taking her from him and burying her face in the soft white fur. 'Danny will be over the moon. I can't believe she came back all by herself.'

'She knows which side her bread is buttered on,' James said with a low laugh. 'Danny must be taking really good care of her.'

'He is,' she said. 'Would you like to come in while I pop her back in her hutch? I can't wait to see Danny's face in the morning.'

'Neither can I. You'll have to video it for me.' He paused. 'I won't come in, thanks. I need to get to bed. But I will do this…'

He took a step closer and gave her a resounding kiss, the rabbit wriggling and squirming between them. It was a long, delicious moment before he released her.

'Let's get you into your hutch,' she told Mary once she'd said goodbye to James, and she took her through the kitchen and out into the yard. When she was satisfied that the rabbit had settled into her hay and was tucking into a belated supper, Edie took herself off to bed.

She was woken a short time later by an odd banging noise coming from outside.

'What now?' she muttered, getting up to investigate, worrying that someone might be trying to break in. Grabbing her sharp dressmaking scissors from the table in the living room as she crept past, she made her way cautiously into the kitchen.

The noises seemed to be coming from Mary's hutch.

Concerned that the little animal might be having some kind of a fit, Edie hastily opened the door and the rabbit launched herself into her arms, snuggling her little furry face into the space between Edie's shoulder and her neck.

Edie's maternal instinct kicked straight in.

'You poor little thing,' she said to the rabbit and, not wanting the bunny to feel even more scared than she already was, she gathered up the litter tray from the kitchen, and took Mary upstairs.

She was smiling as she fell asleep with the bunny tucked in beside her on the bed.

Chapter 24

The house was coming together slowly. Too slowly for James's liking, but without greater funds, he couldn't make the work go any faster.

He was now at an impasse, having to wait until he had enough in his bank account to employ an electrician to do the rewiring, so instead, he concentrated on doing what he could on the land, repairing the drystone walls, and marking out the boundary of the vegetable plot.

He played in the garden for most of the day, in between work commitments, then he visited the local library to make use of their much faster internet to respond to some emails. After that, he was due to take Edie to The Furlongs.

When he called for her, she was carrying an armful of dress, with Danny in tow, holding her work bag.

'Hurry,' she hissed, giving the wedding shop opposite a worried look. 'Mrs C has got a late consultation. She's still in there, and I don't want her to see me with this.' She jerked her head at the dress carrier she was holding.

'Surely she won't know what's in it?' he asked.

Edie gave him an incredulous look. 'She'll know exactly what it is,' she said. 'Let's go.'

She left him to secure the front door and hurried out under the archway, her heels clattering on the cobbles.

James had almost forgotten that Tia's special wedding dress was supposed to be a secret and he, too, shot a furtive glance at Moira's. He couldn't see anyone in the shop, although it was difficult to spot anything beyond the dresses in the window. Still, he thought they'd probably got away with it. And even if they hadn't, surely Mrs Carrington would understand? Edie might very well be going behind her employer's back, but it was for all the best reasons, and he knew she didn't make a habit of it.

He left Edie and Tia cooing over the dress, and took Danny to the stables, having had permission from Edie to let him ride again. The boy was ecstatic but trying to remain calm, having heeded James's instruction that horses were easily excitable at the best of times, and didn't need an excuse to get het up.

To be fair, Pickles was an elderly gent, who'd seen it all before, and a small boy who was almost apoplectic with excitement wasn't going to stop the pony from munching contentedly on his hay.

As James was showing Danny how to tack up the pony, Nick strolled into the barn.

'I saw your car,' he said, 'and guessed you'd brought Edie to see Tia.'

'Yet another fitting.' James rolled his eyes. 'How many does it take?'

Nick shuddered. 'Hundreds, it seems, although Stevie seems to have finally got her dress sorted. Why they can't just go into a shop, pick one, and be done with it, I don't know. If I spent this much time fussing over my suit, I'd never get any work done. As it is, Stevie had a fit over the right colour tie. Apparently, it would be the end of the world if it didn't match the colour of the bridesmaids' dresses.'

James thought back to his suit fitting with William, and shuddered. 'Mate, it sounds horrendous.'

'Don't get me started on the flowers, the cake, the bridal favours—'

'The *what*?'

'Little gifts on the tables. Essential, so I'm told.'

'Really?' James had no idea getting married was so complicated.

'My mummy makes wedding dresses,' Danny piped up, as he checked the girth. James made a note to check it again. Horses and ponies had a tendency to suck in air, blowing out their ribcages so the saddle wasn't as tight as it should be, with the unfortunate result of the saddle shifting and dumping the poor rider on the ground.

'And she's very good at it, too,' he said to Danny. 'Have you seen Tia's dress?' he asked Nick.

'No chance. Tia's barricaded the door. She doesn't want anyone to see it until the day.'

'Is it a secret?' Danny asked.

'Yes, it is,' Nick said, and put a finger to his lips. 'Shhh.' Danny giggled.

'Shall we see what this lad can do?' Nick suggested, hoisting Danny into the saddle and taking hold of the reins. 'That's right, hold them like this, and sit up straight.'

James relinquished control, content to let Nick take charge – he was the expert, after all, having trained more young riders than James had eaten hot dinners.

'Thanks for letting Danny ride,' he said.

'He's doing me a favour,' Nick replied. 'Pickles is getting fat and lazy, so any time you want to ride him,

Danny, feel free. You don't have to ask. Besides,' he turned his attention to James, 'you and Edie are doing Tia a huge favour. She hates the dress that Julia and Mrs Carrington want her to wear, she says it's hideous, but since Edie has designed one for her, she hasn't stopped singing Edie's praises.'

For some reason, James felt inordinately proud of her.

Chapter 25

'Oh, my God! You're kidding, right?' Tia was laughing so hard, she had tears in her eyes.

Edie shook her head. 'I'm not. If anyone had been watching us, they'd have thought it was some kind of comedy sketch. The rabbit, being chased by two dogs, being chased by Danny, then me, then the dogs' owner. We must have looked ridiculous.'

'I can't believe Mary found her way back,' Tia spluttered.

'Neither can I, but thank God she did, because Danny would have been devastated. James made me film his reaction the next morning when he got up to see the bunny snuggled up in my bed.'

'Wait, what?'

'I know; it's not ideal to have a rabbit in bed with you, but the poor little thing was so frightened, and she was demanding cuddles, so I couldn't just—'

'No, I meant James, asking you to film Danny's reaction.'

Edie felt the heat flooding her cheeks.

'Oh, I see. It's like that, is it?' Tia smirked.

'No, it's not.'

'What is it, then?'

Her blush deepened, until she feared she must look like a red traffic light.

'It *is* like that, isn't it?' Tia insisted. 'You never said. *He* never said.' She clapped her hands together. 'I think it's wonderful.'

So did Edie. Especially after the swift kiss he'd given her when he came to pick her up. Danny had caught the tail end of it and had muttered, 'Gross,' under his breath, but Edie could tell that he'd been secretly delighted. She was anticipating the boyfriend question would rear its head again soon, but this time, she wasn't sure how to answer him. *Was* she James's girlfriend? And if not, how was she supposed to describe their relationship?

'How long has it been going on?' Tia asked.

'A few weeks.'

'How does Danny feel about it?'

Tia was certainly direct, Edie thought. 'He adores James,' she said.

'I think you do, too, if the look on your face is any indication.'

'Adore' was probably too strong a word; however, she was beginning to develop deep feelings for him. He was nothing like she'd anticipated when she'd first set eyes on him in Lady Tonbridge's drawing room. He'd seemed to be so at ease there, so sure of himself and his right to be in such grand surroundings. She'd labelled him as posh and entitled, and far too wealthy for her. That was why she'd been so surprised when he'd shown an interest in her.

However, that was before she'd got to know him, and she now realised he was nothing like she'd thought he was. He was kind and thoughtful, taking great pains to ensure Danny was included, and he didn't flaunt his wealth in her face. If she hadn't known any better, she would have assumed he was just like her.

'I like him,' she conceded, aware Tia was waiting for some sort of response.

'Yeah, right, *like*, indeed,' the girl scoffed.

'Can we get back to your dress?' Edie suggested, desperate to change the subject.

'Stuff the dress, your love life is much more fun.'

'I haven't got a love life,' she protested. 'And you won't be so flippant if your dress isn't ready.'

'Seriously, I'm pleased for the pair of you. And you're right about the dress. Will you come to my wedding? Please?'

Edie didn't know what to say. 'Mrs Carrington will attend to you in the morning, to ensure everything's OK,' she said.

'*What?* You mean, *help me get dressed*? Shit. I didn't realise that was part of the service.' Tia began to look concerned.

'She doesn't do it very often; only for her more prestigious brides. Everyone else has to make do with their mum, or sister, or bridesmaids to help them on with their gown.'

'Bugger, I can hardly let her shove me into that monstrosity, then tell her to get out so someone else can manhandle me into this one, can I? I never thought of that. And Julia's probably going to want to help me get ready, too.'

'You can always tell both of them that you don't want them there.'

'I'm going to have to, aren't I, otherwise the cat will be well and truly out of the bag.' Tia looked pleadingly up at her. 'Please say you'll be there? Just you. I don't want anyone, and I mean *anyone*, to see this dress until Nick walks me down the aisle.'

'But what about your bridesmaids? Traditionally, that's what they're there for—'

Tia shook her head, emphatically. 'No, not even them. I don't want anyone to have an inkling I'm wearing anything other than the dress Julia picked.'

Edie thought for a moment. 'I don't see how I can,' she said. 'The wedding is on a Saturday and Mrs Carrington will never let me have the day off, especially if she thinks she should be here.'

'Taking credit for a dress you did all the work on, you mean, even if the dress is nasty.'

Edie giggled. 'It's not nasty – it's just not the right one for you.'

'Oh, sorry, I guess you designed that one, too?'

'Actually, I didn't. It's a fairly basic shape, and the fabric is nothing special.'

'Julia's a cheapskate,' Tia muttered.

'Oh, believe me, the dress isn't cheap,' Edie said. 'Not at Moira's prices.'

Tia rolled her eyes. 'Why would Julia want to pay all that money for something so boring?' She glanced down at herself. 'You can't call this dress boring.'

Edie had to agree with her; it was already looking divine, and that was without all the beading which had yet to be painstakingly sewn on, one by time-consuming one.

'I still want you to dress me,' Tia insisted.

'Mrs Carrington will be there,' Edie maintained. 'And, as I said, she's not going to let me have the time off.'

'Sod Mrs Carrington. I'm going to decide who dresses me, not her or Julia.'

Edie bit her lip.

'Oh, sorry. I wasn't thinking, was I? Of course, you can't dress me, else your sour-faced boss will realise you made me another, better dress.'

She nodded, grateful that Tia understood.

'OK, we'll keep it to ourselves for a while longer,' Tia said. 'I'll tell Julia that the bridesmaids are going to help me get ready, and that I don't want her or Moira Carrington there. I'll leave it until the very last minute to tell Leanne, Stevie and Melissa about the replacement dress.'

'Will Melissa say anything to her mother, though?'

'Not if I'm fashionably late.' Tia had a wicked glint in her eye. 'There won't be enough time to do anything but stuff me into it. Can you keep it at your place until the morning of the wedding? James will probably be tied up with William – not literally, I hope, unless that's the only way James can think of to prevent my gorgeous husband-to-be from doing a runner. I'll send Nick over to collect it; he's in on the secret, so I'm sure he won't mind.'

Edie was relieved at the solution. Even now, at this late stage and with the end in sight, she still couldn't rid herself of the uneasy feeling that Mrs C knew there was something up. Or was it her conscience making her feel this way?

It didn't matter – it would all soon be over, and she vowed that she was never, ever going to do anything like this ever again. Her nerves simply couldn't stand it.

Chapter 26

The day of the Tanglewood Summer Fete dawned bright and sunny. At eight o'clock in the morning, there was already a hint of the warmth to come, Edie thought, as she sat in the yard, sipping her tea. Danny, as expected, was already up, brushing Mary to within an inch of her life, in preparation for her participation in the rabbit race later. He was on pins until it was time to go, pestering her constantly, until she gave in and agreed to set off, even though they had a couple of hours before the race was scheduled to start.

She had a fight on her hands to persuade him to leave Mary in her hutch for the time being, not wanting to carry the rabbit around for ages, and worried that the poor thing would have sensory overload way before the event began.

'We'll come back for her later,' she told him, and he had to be satisfied with that.

James was due to meet them there, and as soon as they walked through the gate and onto the field, she began looking for him.

Crikey, but it was busy, thronging with villagers and visitors alike. The fete always drew a good crowd, and with the especially good weather this year, it was more crowded than usual.

Danny, always hungry, dragged her towards a hot dog stand (she'd promised him one for lunch) and he devoured his in three bites. She gave him her untouched one too, even though she was hungry herself; she didn't want to buy him another one because she knew she needed to save her pennies for all the other things he'd no doubt want to have a go at, like the coconut shy.

They wandered around, enjoying the festive atmosphere. The fete was an odd combination of county show and funfair, with a showjumping ring, dressage and scurry racing for the horsey-minded, tombola, lucky dip stalls, dog agility and much more.

She bought a bag of hot, crunchy doughnuts, liberally sprinkled with sugar, and they found a couple of plastic fold-up seats to sit on while they tucked in.

Afterwards, Danny, still licking the stickiness from his fingers, dragged her towards the tent where the rabbits and other small animals were being shown.

'We could have entered Mary in this,' he said. 'She's pretty.'

'Do rabbits have to have pedigrees, like dogs do?' she wondered, admiring a tiny black and white lop-eared bunny, with a heart-shaped splodge around his nose.

Danny dashed from one cage to the next, comparing each occupant with his beloved pet and then, when he'd finally had his fill of small cute things, he dragged her off to view the horses in the show ring.

'Wow!' For once, her son was lost for words, and so was she.

The horses being led around the arena were the largest she'd ever seen, even though she'd brought Danny to the fete every year since he'd been born.

'They're Shire horses,' she said, listening to the tannoy. 'These are the boy horses; stallions, they're called.'

The one passing right by where they were standing towered over her. The guy holding the horse wasn't exactly short (possibly six foot) and his head only just reached to the beast's shoulder.

'I'm glad Pickles isn't that big, but maybe when I'm older, I'll be able to ride one of those?' Danny looked up at her with a hopeful expression.

'Maybe one day,' she agreed, thinking it was unlikely. The only way her son would get to ride anything other than Pickles was if Nick let him have a go on one of his precious showjumpers, and she couldn't see that happening. They were too expensive to risk sticking a small boy, who had no idea what he was doing, on their valuable backs.

He was equally fascinated by the duck herding ('No, Danny, you can't have a duck'), the wood-carving competition using chainsaws ('I don't think so, do you?') and the pole climbing ('Nope – no way'). But she did say yes to him having a go on the climbing wall when she saw that other children were allowed on, and after she'd had a good look at the safety equipment the instructors were using on their young charges.

After he was strapped into a harness of some sort, Edie watched him with her heart in her mouth, as he climbed slowly but steadily up the fake rockface, then abseiled down.

Dear God, she might feel inordinately proud of him, but she didn't think her nerves could take any more of this. 'How about watching the Punch and Judy show?'

she asked, having heard the unmistakable voices of the puppets from a booth nearby.

Danny gave her a scornful look. 'That's for babies,' he stated. 'I want to go on the big wheel. Or – *that!*'

'That' was a giant pendulum arm, with seats at one end which were in the process of being swung up and down, and round and round. Edie's stomach turned over just from looking at it, and she was fairly certain that she would actually be sick if she went on it. There was no question of her letting Danny go on by himself, so if she was seriously considering allowing him to go on the ride, then she'd have to go on, too, and she'd probably run the risk of losing the doughnuts she'd just eaten.

All the while, Edie had been scanning the crowd, hoping for a glimpse of James, but so far he was nowhere to be seen; then she spotted him and her stomach did a little flip.

She was about to suggest to Danny that James might be persuaded to go on the ride, which was rather worryingly called Kamikaze, when she saw who he was talking to and her heart dropped to her trainers.

He had his head back, laughing at something Leanne Green was saying and, although Leanne and Rex were most definitely an item, Edie couldn't help but remember the conversation between Leanne and Stevie's other bridesmaid, Karen from London.

James hadn't mentioned anything about him being invited to Stevie and Nick's wedding, but it was entirely possible that he had been. She had a vision of James getting friendly with a certain pretty, dark-haired bridesmaid, and hot jealousy rose up to swamp her.

Steadfastly, Edie turned away, trying not to let either of them see she was watching, and she pretended to concentrate on a small, yappy dog, who was dashing around the agility course in the ring opposite, and totally ignoring the calls of his irate owner. The crowd was laughing, and Edie forced a smile to her lips, not wanting to let Danny see that she was starting to become upset. It was irrational, she knew, but she couldn't help it. She'd never cared for any man enough to be bothered if he looked at someone else. Not even Danny's father, she realised. That particular relationship had been nothing but a silly, teenage crush, with a life-changing outcome. Her discovery that she was pregnant had swiftly seen the demise of her crush on him, as had the boy's reaction to her news. His parents hadn't been particularly pleased either, she recalled bitterly. But then, neither had her mother, because it had been a case of history repeating itself.

A kiss on the back of her neck made her jump, jolting her out of her less-than-pleasant thoughts.

'Got you,' James said, his arms snaking around her waist, and she leant into him, the back of her head resting against his chest as he stood behind her. Despite herself, she couldn't help glancing around to see if Leanne Green had noticed, but the florist was nowhere in sight.

With James at her side, the day grew steadily better, as they strolled hand-in-hand around the fete, occasionally stopping at the stalls or rides that caught Danny's interest (the cake stall and the helter-skelter were firm favourites, and even James hadn't fancied the Kamikaze ride). Edie was simply content to be in James's company, his strong hand wrapped firmly around hers. Every so often, his fingers would stroke her skin, sending a shiver through her.

When the time came for the rabbit racing, she gave him her house key, and he went to fetch Mary. Then the all-important race was finally about to begin and Danny, with a pocket full of carrot chunks, positioned himself near the end of the racetrack, which consisted of seven straight lines with bales of hay separating them. A crowd of eager spectators had already gathered.

There seemed to be a great deal of active betting taking place, with a pretty black and white floppy-eared bunny being the firm favourite – Edie had a suspicion that it was the same one she'd admired in the judging tent, but she couldn't get a good glimpse of its nose to check whether there was a heart-shaped splodge on it or not.

James handed Mary to her and Edie stood at the start, holding the struggling rabbit in her arms. The bunny was eager for her carrot treat, having only been given half her usual portion of breakfast this morning, and was desperate to get down. Or it could have been the fact that many of the spectators had dogs with them. They were on leads, but Edie was conscious of the last time the rabbit had seen a dog, and she hoped the sight of so many canines wouldn't put Mary off, considering her recent encounter with a pair of Dalmatians.

'Are you ready?' the compère called. 'Are your rabbits ready? After the count of three, I want you to put your bunnies on the ground.'

Several people who'd done this kind of thing before were leaning over the barrier, holding their charges just above the grass. With Danny jumping up and down at the far end, Edie did the same.

'One, two, three. Go!' the tannoy announced.

Edie released Mary, and the rabbit immediately began to hop towards Danny. Unfortunately, a couple of other better-trained rabbits, who knew the score and weren't as easily distracted by the sight of other bunnies, the yelling spectators, or the dogs, took off down the track as if they were wind-up toys.

'Go, Mary!' Edie yelled at the top of her voice, jumping up and down more than Danny had been a few moments earlier.

Everyone was yelling for their favourite contender, and she could hear James behind her, shouting just as loudly. It was a wonder Mary could hear Danny's voice above the commotion, but she did. Inexorably, if somewhat slowly, the rabbit made her way down the track, with the occasional pause to investigate the bales of hay and the occupants of the track either side, as she balanced on her back legs, her front paws on the top of a bale, her nose twitching as she tried to peer over the top of it.

Edie could hear Danny calling, 'Come here, Mary, come on, good girl.' His hand was outstretched as far as it could go, a glimmer of orange in his palm, and he was leaning so far over the barrier that Edie thought he might topple over.

The floppy-eared rabbit got to the end before Mary was even halfway down the track and then, much to Danny's disgust, hopped over the bales separating the two lanes, to snatch the chunk of carrot out of Danny's hand. Edie collapsed in a fit of giggles, and she was still giggling when she made her way to the end to rescue a rather disgruntled Danny, who was struggling to hold a wriggling Mary.

'I'll take her back, shall I?' James offered, and Edie gratefully handed him her keys again.

This time he was gone rather longer and she began to worry that something had happened to him, but eventually he found her and his hand slipped into hers.

The rest of the afternoon passed in a blur of colour, noise and assorted smells (many of them being of either the farmyard or the cooking variety, depending on where you were standing), but the only things Edie was conscious of were the solidity of the man at her side, the scent of his aftershave which occasionally wafted over her, and the feel of his strong hand in hers.

While they were watching Danny trying to hit tin cans off shelves, and not getting very far, her knees went weak when James bent his head to say, 'I'll win a prize for him,' as he gave her a fleetingly wonderful kiss.

Having dutifully won a prize as promised, and handing the child's fishing rod and net to Danny, James caught hold of her and kissed her again, another featherlight, quick meeting of their lips. After the lovely time they'd had it was only natural that she invited him back to join her and Danny for an early supper of pasta and salad.

When she walked into her kitchen, she saw what had taken him so long earlier, when he'd taken Mary back to her hutch. A huge bunch of wildflowers sat in her sink, tied with a couple of grass stems.

'Leanne Green had better watch out,' she laughed, delighted. 'You'll give her a run for her money.'

'It was her idea,' he said. 'I was going to get you roses, but she said, given my job, this was more appropriate. I picked them myself,' he added, proudly, 'and tied them.'

He showed her his finger, which had a tiny cut on it from the stems of grass he'd used in lieu of ribbon. Impulsively, touched beyond measure by the flowers (no one had ever given her flowers before), she reached for his hand and brought it up to her lips, kissing the injured digit.

'If I found some other injuries, would you kiss those too?' He pointed to his mouth. 'My lips are sore.'

'We can't have that, can we?' she murmured, and stood on tiptoe.

James bent his head, and when his lips touched hers, a bolt of electricity shot through her as their kiss deepened.

'Damn it, woman, do you realise the effect you're having on me?' he muttered into her mouth.

'Uh, huh,' she replied, too busy kissing him better to make a proper reply.

Conscious that Danny was checking on Mary and would be back any second, she reluctantly pulled away, and stepped back.

'Aw...' he said.

'You sound like Danny when I tell him he can't have another biscuit,' she giggled.

'You're mean,' he said to her.

'You can have another one later,' she promised.

'Just one?'

'That depends on whether you eat all your tea.'

'Crikey, Danny's got it tough,' he joked.

But James *did* eat all his tea, and Edie kept her promise.

Chapter 27

James was nervous, an emotion so alien to him that it took him by surprise. It's only dinner, he tried to tell himself. It wasn't as though he'd never taken a woman out for a meal before.

But this was Edie, and he very much wanted to impress her. It was their first date without Danny, and they were doing grown-up things, like going out in the evening and having dinner, with wine.

OK, she'd be having wine – he had to drive them to the restaurant and back, then get himself home afterwards. Walking wasn't an option, he knew, especially when he set eyes on Edie and her heels.

'Wow. Just wow.'

From the laughter on her face, he guessed he must have said that out loud. She looked absolutely stunning, in a flowing silky dress that seemed to cling in all the right places. Her usual messy (but very sweet) bun had been replaced by long hair, straight and glossy, falling over her shoulders and halfway down her back. She was wearing make-up, too, not that she needed it, and high heels with pink-painted toes peeping through the silver straps.

'Wow!'

'You just said that,' she giggled.

'I might say it again,' he smiled. 'You look gorgeous.'

'Thank you, kind sir. I thought I'd make a bit of an effort.' She trailed off, and his heart leapt. It looked like she felt the significance of their first proper date, too. Alone, just the two of them. The evening was full of possibilities.

Dipping into the limited funds available to him, he'd done as William had originally suggested, and had booked a table at The Griffin. The restaurant was a former farmhouse, beautifully converted, and it had a Michelin star rating (he knew all about those, because Julia Ferris was in hot pursuit of one for The Manor). The outside of the building was strung with twinkling fairy lights, and although the sun hadn't completely set yet, the glow emanating from the windows was warm and enticing.

A waiter showed them to a table with a flourish, pulling a chair out for Edie, who appeared startled at first and then delighted. She gazed around, her eyes everywhere, drinking it all in, reinforcing his impression that she didn't eat out a great deal, and certainly not in places like this. It made him even more determined to ensure she was spoilt rotten this evening and had a thoroughly enjoyable time, even if it did bankrupt him. Edie deserved the best, and James wanted to give it to her. It was just a pity that his bank account wasn't as keen on the idea. Thanks to his parents, he knew what 'the best' looked like, but unlike William and nearly every other boy in that hideously expensive private school he'd attended, his mum and dad had been forced to scrimp and save to send him there. James had come out of it with a pretty decent education and a firm grasp of the value of money.

'Is everything OK?' Edie broke into his thoughts.

'It's wonderful,' he said, hastening to drive the concern from her face. 'I was just wondering if you preferred red, white, or rosé.'

'Um, rosé, I think. I don't drink much.' She uttered a small laugh. 'If you had to get up at the crack of dawn with a hyperactive child, you'd understand why.'

'Do you ever get a lie-in?'

She shook her head. 'Although I daresay when Danny hits the teenage years, I'll have the opposite problem and won't be able to get him out of bed.'

'I remember what I used to be like,' he confessed. 'Awake half the night and asleep half the morning. I read somewhere that teenagers can't help it. It's something to do with their brains being rewired before they enter adulthood.'

'I don't think Mother Nature did a particularly good job on rewiring mine,' she joked. 'It feels permanently scrambled.'

'I'm not surprised. You're holding down a job and bringing up a child at the same time. And from what I can see, I don't believe your Mrs Carrington is the most sympathetic of employers.'

She giggled, the sound warming his heart. 'You can say that again! But I do love what I do, so I consider myself lucky. So many people are in jobs they hate. Mine might be hard work, but it's so rewarding.'

'Tia certainly seems impressed. She's been singing your praises to me.'

He watched a slow blush spread across her cheeks. Tia had been doing more than extolling Edie's skill as a designer and seamstress. She'd led him to believe that Edie really liked him, but when he'd pushed her for more information, she'd become rather tight-lipped, much to his annoyance.

'That reminds me,' he said. 'You know that I'm William's best man? I'd like you to accompany me to their wedding.'

Edie lowered her gaze and began to fiddle with her wine glass, twisting the stem with her fingers. She didn't say anything for a while, and James wondered if he'd spoken out of turn.

Then she looked up and met his gaze and shook her head wistfully. 'I'd love to, but I can't. I work Saturdays, and Mrs Carrington's not going to let me have the time off. Especially since she was expecting to be there to help Tia get dressed.'

'Eh?' He was baffled. He knew Tia sometimes struggled with certain things, but he wasn't sure that getting dressed was one of them.

Edie smiled. 'Wedding dresses are quite delicate and can be tricky little blighters to get on and off. Often, there can be loads of tiny buttons or hooks and eyes, and the bride normally has her make-up and hair done before donning the dress. Even if the dress doesn't have intricate fastenings, she'd normally need help to get it over her head without trashing her hair, her make-up, or the dress.'

'Blimey! This getting married business isn't straightforward, is it?'

'It is for the groom,' she retorted dryly.

'Do you think you'll design your own dress, you know, when the time comes?'

'Oh, I'm not getting married,' she replied. 'I've got Danny to consider.'

James thought that while her attitude might be admirable, and of course her son would always come first, she was being short-sighted. She was still so young; many women her age hadn't even begun to think of settling down yet, and Danny was growing up fast. In only a few short years, he'd be wanting to spend less and less time with her, until eventually he'd move out, to live his own life.

Of course, she'd not be too old to find love – no one ever was, in his opinion – but he hoped, *prayed*, that she wasn't too blinkered by her maternal responsibilities that she'd dismiss love when it came knocking.

Because it had certainly tapped on his heart. He was beginning to have quite deep feelings for the woman sitting opposite him.

'Maybe one day you'll feel differently,' he said lightly, his tone at odds with his emotions. He very much hoped she'd change her mind. Not about marriage – of course, it was far too early to be contemplating anything so serious – but about love and relationships. Maybe, he hoped, she was already starting to come around a little, because she had let him kiss her, and she'd agreed to go out with him tonight on what was very clearly a date. They'd most definitely progressed beyond the just-friends stage. Just-friends didn't kiss the way she'd kissed him back. Just-friends didn't cause his heart to pound whenever he thought about her, or make his head spin when he caught the elusive scent of her perfume on his clothes, or when he remembered the feel of her when he held her, or the depths in her eyes, when he gazed into them—

'The menu, sir.'

James came back to earth with a jolt as a menu was placed in front of him. Edie had already opened hers and was examining it with a frown on her face, and he wondered if there was a problem. He opened his own. Despite knowing the restaurant was expensive – Michelin stars didn't come cheap – James still had to work hard not to wince when he saw the prices. Ouch.

To give his wallet time to recover from the palpitations from which it was undoubtedly suffering, he remembered what they'd been talking about before his heart had decided to ambush him, and suggested, 'How about coming to the evening bash, instead? It'll be much more fun anyway, with all the awkward posing for photos and the embarrassing speeches out of the way.'

James wasn't actually sure just how much fun it would be, because he wasn't all that keen on formal occasions, but it would definitely be more fun with Edie by his side.

'We'll see,' she said, and he'd heard her utter the same phrase, using the same tone, when talking to Danny, when she meant 'no' but didn't want to discuss it.

He let it go for now. After a couple more dates, she might be more amenable to the idea, so he changed the subject and they chatted about the films they liked, the music they had in common, the books they'd read. Unsurprisingly, Edie had a strong interest in high-end fashion and haute couture (he still wasn't sure he understood what that was, even after she'd explained it to him) but she also liked art, and she told him that sometimes she got inspiration for designs from old paintings. He quite liked visiting art galleries, but he tended to prefer the more modern stuff, and as for films, their tastes differed wildly. He'd expected her to like romcoms (silly, he knew), but she confessed that she preferred shoot-'em-ups and action films. James had a penchant for film noir, and he quite enjoyed many of the older films, those which had been shot in black and white.

The evening passed in a blur of chat and laughter; the only sticking point had been when Edie opened the menu, but she'd soon rallied and had become even more talkative after her second glass of wine.

'I'm not used to this much alcohol,' she giggled, and he realised she was a bit tipsy.

To be honest, neither was he. He'd never been a heavy drinker, although he'd had his moments in his youth, but these days he preferred to keep a level head. Along with the purchase of his first property, he took it as a sign he was growing up. About time, too, his mum would probably say.

It was as they were leaving, James opening the door for her to walk through ahead of him, that Edie stopped. When she glanced back at him, he noticed the worry on her face and he looked beyond her to see what had caused it.

Mrs Carrington was standing in the foyer, waiting to enter the restaurant, and her eyes were boring into Edie. Slowly, she turned her attention to him.

'Edie,' Moira Carrington said, looking back at her. 'I didn't expect to see you here.'

'I'm with James,' she said hesitantly.

He could tell she was nervous by the set of her shoulders, and he decided to take charge. Stepping forward, he held out his hand. Mrs Carrington paused before she took it.

'James Preece, William Ferris's best man,' he said, her hand lying limply in his own firm grip. 'We met at The Manor, but I'm not sure whether we were formally introduced.' He had his public school voice on, one he didn't use very often but which usually impressed those types of people who considered that kind of thing important.

'Moira Carrington. Nice to meet you,' she replied.

James had the impression she only found it 'nice' because of his connection to The Manor. And also, she had no real idea who he was, except that she'd seen him wander into Julia Ferris's drawing room with William, appearing completely at home there. He *did* feel at home in The Manor, because he'd spent many a holiday there, and then, after travelling extensively and living in some odd places, he had developed the ability to make himself feel at home anywhere. But Edie's employer didn't know that, and he'd got the impression from Edie that status meant a great deal to good old Mrs C.

'Well, then,' Mrs Carrington said to Edie. 'I'll see you tomorrow, bright and early.' She gave James a dignified nod which he returned.

'Of course,' Edie said. 'I'll be in at the usual time.'

'Make sure you are,' the woman said.

Edie inhaled sharply and slapped a hand to her mouth. '*Oh*, I'll… um… have to bring Danny with me,' she said in a rush as Mrs Carrington began to walk through the door which James was holding open for her. 'I'm sorry, I forgot to mention it earlier, but his school has got a teacher training day, and my mum has a hospital appointment, so…'

Edie looked stricken, and he could tell she hated having to do this.

'I've got something on first thing,' he offered, 'but I could pick him up at eleven thirty-ish, if that's OK with you.' He'd need to juggle a few things around, but if it meant helping Edie (and getting to see her again tomorrow), he was more than willing.

Edie, two spots of colour on her cheeks, looked at him gratefully. 'That would be wonderful.'

'Don't make a habit of it,' Mrs C said, before sweeping into the restaurant without a backward glance, her head held high, her back ramrod straight.

Edie waited until they'd reached James's car before she sagged against him. 'I *don't* make a habit of it,' she protested, unshed tears making her eyes shine.

'Why is she so horrible?' he demanded, angry on Edie's behalf. She deserved to be treated better than that.

'She's like that with most people,' Edie said, 'except for those who she thinks are better than her, like you and Lady Tonbridge.'

James snorted. Like him, indeed – if only she knew… 'Christ, even Julia Ferris isn't as bad as her, and she's got a title and has far more reason to be hoity-toity,' he observed.

'I should have asked her earlier about bringing Danny into work, but I forgot.' Edie sounded mortified.

'It's not as though you do it all the time,' he said, trying to mollify her, 'and I bet Danny's as good as gold.'

'He is!' she agreed. 'He sits up in my workroom with his books or a comic and is as quiet as a church mouse.'

'So, what's her problem?'

'She hates kids. I'm pretty sure she doesn't like me much, either.'

'Who could fail to like you?' He moved closer and wrapped his arms around her, then dipped his head down to hers, to brush her lips with a light kiss.

'That's not all, is it?' he said when she didn't respond, and she let out a soft wail.

'I'm worried she'll find out that I'm making a wedding dress for Tia. If she does, she'll sack me.'

'I'm sure she wouldn't. *Would she?*'

Edie nodded. 'She most definitely would.'

'Even though you're doing it on your own time?' He didn't understand what the issue was. OK, so Edie was making Tia a second dress, but it wasn't as though she didn't intend to pay for the first one. Mrs Carrington would have her money, Tia would have the dress she wanted, and Edie would get paid for making it. The only person who might be a bit miffed, in his opinion, was Julia, and that would only be because she was a bit of a control freak.

'Mrs Carrington would see it as a conflict of interest,' Edie was saying, 'especially since it was Lady Tonbridge who commissioned the dress from Moira's. She'll see it as a snub, and when Tia appears in the gown I made, Mrs C won't be able to take the credit, either.'

'But if you hadn't agreed to make this one for Tia, she would simply have gone elsewhere. You were doing her a favour.'

'I don't think Mrs C will look at it like that.'

'It's lucky only you, me, Tia, and Nick know, then, isn't it? You can deny all knowledge on the day, and even if she suspects, she doesn't have any proof,' he said.

But for all his reasonable words, Edie's obvious worry had stirred his own. He hadn't been looking forward to William and Tia's wedding before this; now all he wanted was for it to be over, and for Edie to stop fretting.

Chapter 28

The following morning didn't start particularly well, with Danny out of sorts, and not his usual sunny self.

'Why can't I stay here with Mary?' he demanded. 'I'm old enough.'

Edie was hearing that a lot from him lately, and it pained her to see how quickly he was growing up and how desperately he wanted to be independent. But at eight years of age, there was no way she was leaving him on his own in the house, even if she was only a short walk away.

'Pack a couple of books,' she told him. 'It won't be for long because James is coming to fetch you at eleven thirty.'

Edie was incredibly picky about who she allowed to look after her son, and she'd surprised herself by how readily she'd agreed to let Danny spend the rest of the day with James. After all, she didn't know that much about the guy, even though they'd shared several very nice (heart-stopping, incredible, wonderful) kisses, apart from the fact that he'd gone to school with William, he'd worked abroad for several years, and had now bought the old Hopkins place.

The old farmhouse had been on the market for a number of years, and she'd been surprised when James said he was the one who'd bought it. Even though it was a fair distance out of the village, everyone had known Mr

Hopkins because he used to be a regular in the high street, usually in The Hen and Duck. Word had it that he'd had to go into a home and hadn't taken a great deal of care of his property for several years before he'd had to vacate it, and everyone had said it was in an awful state.

She couldn't imagine James living there, but he'd told her he was in the middle of doing it up. She would like to see it before the work was carried out, and then afterwards, to compare. She loved those programmes on TV where people would buy complete and utter sheds, then do them up. The before and after shots were the best bits.

'Can I take my paints?' Danny asked.

'Certainly not!' Edie shuddered, a vision of spilt paint over pristine white fabric popping into her mind. He scowled, but she knew he'd only asked out of devilment, not expecting her to agree.

He'd become a little more reasonable and less grumpy by the time they crossed the courtyard and unlocked the front door to Moira's, so she settled him into the workroom and trotted back downstairs to do her usual chores for the day before Mrs C was due to swan in at eleven o'clock, her normal time for putting in an appearance.

Edie examined the appointment book, seeing there was a new client due in at noon, and before that, a bride whose wedding was a week Saturday was due in for a final fitting.

She groaned when she saw the name – Beatrice Fisher. Miss Fisher had a bit of a weight problem, in that she couldn't seem to keep it stable. The poor dress had been taken in and let out more times than Edie cared to count. She'd had a feeling that might be the case when, during the initial consultation, the bride had informed her that she intended to lose two stone by her big day, and her mother had laughed and rolled her eyes. Edie had thought the girl looked lovely as she was and didn't need to lose any weight, but she knew better than to say anything, especially with Mrs Carrington in the room.

She retrieved the dress in question and hung it in the spacious fitting room ready for the client, then she popped back upstairs to check on Danny.

He was sitting on a chair in the corner, well out of the way and reading a book, with a packet of crisps and a drink on a table next to him.

Satisfied that he was behaving himself, she readied the big books of fabric swatches, stacking them neatly on a side table in the viewing area, and switched the coffee machine on.

As soon as Mrs Carrington arrived, Edie slipped back upstairs to work on alterations for a set of bridesmaids' dresses, until her employer called her down to see Miss Fisher and her incredible shrinking and expanding dress.

She had several pins in her mouth and was concentrating on ensuring the waistline was perfect, when she spotted Danny out of the corner of her eye.

With a sigh, she straightened to tell him to go back upstairs, but then she saw his face and her stomach plummeted to her shoes.

He was pale, his eyes were huge, and he looked petrified.

She knew immediately that something awful had happened. 'What?' she whispered, terrified of his answer but needing to know. 'Excuse me a second,' she said to

Miss Fisher, and hurried over to him, taking the pins out of her mouth with shaking fingers.

'I've spilt my juice,' he informed her in a small voice.

Edie breathed a sigh of relief. Was that all? His seat was far enough away from the piles of fabric and the dresses hanging on the rails, all in various stages of completion, for a spot of spilt orange juice not to be a problem.

'Get a cloth from the loo and wipe it up,' she told him, her pulse slowing and the tingling in her fingers from the sudden adrenalin rush dissipating. He'd nearly given her heart failure.

He didn't move, just continued to stare at her with a stricken expression, and suddenly she knew what he was about to tell her wasn't going to be good.

'Where did you spill it?' she asked slowly, dread clutching at her heart and twisting her stomach.

'On Tia's dress.'

Oh, God…

'How do you know it's Tia's?' she asked, realising it was a silly question even as she asked it. The dresses were all labelled, and Danny could read perfectly well enough. 'Never mind. Danny, why were you near the dresses? I thought I told you to stay put? Oh, God, what am I going to do?'

'I'm sorry, I just wanted to see it, because Tia said it was hideous. But it doesn't matter, does it, Mummy, because you made her a much nicer one.'

'Danny—' she began, but Mrs Carrington's voice cut across her. Edie jumped. Oh shit, she'd thought Mrs C was in the viewing area, not standing right behind her.

'Do I understand this correctly?' her employer demanded, her voice icily cold. 'Not only have you allowed your son to ruin a perfectly good and extremely expensive dress, but you've made the client a second dress, and the client, Lady Tonbridge's future daughter-in-law, thinks the dress we chose for her is hideous. Have I got that right?'

Unfortunately, she had. She'd summed up the situation very succinctly.

Edie nodded, tears gathering in her eyes and threatening to spill over.

Mrs Carrington was also succinct when she said the following words:

'You're sacked.'

Chapter 29

James was just about to get in his car to collect Danny when a phone call interrupted his pleasant thoughts about seeing Edie later. It was Tia.

'Hello, my lovely, what can I do for you?' he asked.

'The shit has hit the fan,' she said bluntly.

'In what way?'

'Julia and that awful Mrs Carrington found out about the second dress.'

'*What?* How?'

'There was an orange juice incident involving Danny and dress number one.'

'I don't understand.'

'Even worse, Mrs Carrington has sacked Edie.'

'Aw, damn it.'

'Exactly.'

James ran a hand through his hair, worry knotting his stomach. He wondered why Edie hadn't phoned to tell him herself. 'Have you spoken to Edie? Is that how you found out?'

'Julia rang me,' Tia said. 'She was in a right tizzy, demanding to know what was going on. Moira Carrington had called and she was furious. I had to come clean; Mrs Carrington knew the details anyway.'

'Poor Edie.' James sighed.

'I feel awful. She was only doing me a favour and now she's lost her job because of it.'

'I was going to pick Danny up from Moira's and take him out for the rest of the day, so I'll go to see Edie now. She must be in a right state.'

She was, he saw, when she answered the door and hope flared briefly in her eyes, only for it to dim when she realised it was him. He guessed she'd been hoping it was Mrs Carrington, come to offer her the job back.

Without saying anything, he took her into his arms, holding her close and nuzzling her hair. The gesture proved too much for her, and she sobbed into his chest.

'We'll work something out,' he crooned when she'd calmed somewhat, having no idea what. 'Maybe if I speak to Mrs Carrington—'

'Don't bother,' she hiccupped. 'It's hopeless. I knew the risk if she found out. She's got every right to sack me.'

'But if you explained—?'

'I tried. She didn't want to know. She said it was gross misconduct, and she's right. Oh, what am I going to do?'

'Something will turn up.'

'It won't, I know it won't.'

'It will,' he insisted, resisting the juvenile urge to cross his fingers.

'I've ruined everything.'

'No, you haven't,' he insisted. 'You can still sew. What's to stop you from working for yourself?'

She let go of him and stepped back. Her eyes brimmed with tears, and the skin of her lightly tanned face was blotchy.

'Money,' she said shortly. 'I can't afford the material. Hell, I can't even afford to catch the train to Bristol to buy the material. And I don't have any clients, or a proper workspace. The cottage is barely big enough for me and Danny as it is, without having half a dozen dresses around the place.'

James opened his mouth to say she could work at his house. Then closed it again, as he realised what a silly idea that was. He might be able to put up with the less than pristine conditions in his place, but he couldn't expect Edie to – delicate white gowns and dirt didn't mix.

'Besides,' she added, 'the letting agreement states quite clearly that business activities aren't allowed.' Her eyes widened with renewed fear. 'Oh, God, I've already been working from home, haven't I, on Tia's dress. What if Eastern Estates find out? I could lose my home.'

She burst into fresh sobs, and James gathered her to him again, feeling like sobbing himself. To see her so distressed was breaking his heart. She didn't deserve this.

Briefly, anger at what Mrs Carrington had done flared in his chest. He was annoyed with Julia Ferris, too. If the pair of them hadn't railroaded Tia into wearing a wedding dress she didn't like, then none of this would have happened. Tia, as she'd rightly said, carried her fair share of the blame, too. Tia was feisty enough to stand up to Julia; she really should have made her feelings clear and put her foot down in the beginning. He knew her reasons why, but they now appeared trivial when faced with Edie's anguish.

'I should have said no,' Edie cried. 'I knew it was wrong, but a bride deserves to feel like a princess on her wedding day.'

Edie was right, too – she should have said no, but she'd done what she'd done for the kindest of reasons.

Besides, pointing fingers wouldn't change the situation.

'How's Danny?' he asked. The poor little lad must be mortified.

'Confused, bewildered. He knows he shouldn't have touched Tia's dress, but I shouldn't have put him in that position in the first place. He's only a child, after all. It didn't help that he told Mrs C that ruining Tia's dress didn't matter because I'd made her another one.'

'Oh, dear.'

'Exactly. She also heard him saying that Tia called the first dress hideous. But it's not his fault,' she insisted. 'It's mine.'

'Where is he now?'

'With Mary.'

'I'll go and see him, shall I?'

'I'll put the kettle on.' She wiped her eyes, brushing her tears away with a quick, impatient dash of her hand.

'We *will* sort something out,' he insisted.

'We?'

'Do you honestly think I'll leave you to sort this mess out on your own? It's partly my fault you're in this predicament in the first place.'

'How do you work that out?'

'I'm the one who's been ferrying you back and forth to The Furlongs.'

She gave a small, sad smile. 'I don't think my lack of transport would have put Tia off, do you?'

'I suppose not,' he admitted.

Tia Saunders could be one determined lady when she put her mind to it. William had told him that he'd had a devil's job to convince Tia that he loved her. She'd been adamant that he'd come to regret marrying someone who was disabled, and that she was ruining his life. She'd intended to move out of The Furlongs, where she'd been living with Nick, and move back in with her mother to set William free. She'd only relented and accepted that they were soulmates when William had told her wherever she went, that was where he intended to be, and that he'd follow her to the ends of the earth if he had to.

James went outside, and after having a long conversation with a distraught Danny to convince him that his mum wasn't upset with him, returned to the cottage to find Edie manically cleaning the kitchen. She had her head in the oven, a pair of pink rubber gloves on, and her bum sticking up in the air. Although it mightn't be the right time to ogle her curves, he found he couldn't help himself.

Feeling rather ashamed, he coughed politely to let her know he was there, but she'd been so lost in her thoughts that he made her jump.

'Ow!' she said, bumping her head on the edge of the oven as she extracted herself from it.

'What are you doing?'

'Cleaning the oven.' She sounded cross.

'Why now?'

'Because it needs doing, and I've got lots of time on my hands.'

James gently took the cloth from her. 'Why don't we get out of here and take a walk, to clear our heads?' he offered.

'But the oven—'

'It can wait.'

She herself had said she had plenty of time now. She could do it tomorrow, or the day after. Or—

'Why are you really going overboard on the cleaning?' he asked, wondering why she felt the need to do it right now.

Tears welled in her eyes again and she blinked furiously. 'Because if I'm evicted, I'll have to leave the cottage spotless or I'll lose my deposit.'

He blinked. What on earth made her think she was going to be evicted? 'That's not going to happen,' he said. 'And even if by the remotest chance it did, your landlord would have to give you a month's notice.'

'If I don't find another job soon, I won't be able to afford the rent.' She grimaced. 'I clean when I'm upset,' she admitted.

'Clean later. I've got the rest of the day free, so let's get out of here.' He paused. 'Would you like to see my house? I warn you, it's not up to much and I may bully you into picking up a hammer and knocking some of the old plaster off. It's way more fun than cleaning the oven.' He gave her an ingratiating smile. 'I can even provide ice-cold water for washing afterwards.'

He could see her mind whirring, and guessed she was torn between wanting to remain in her cottage, trying to regain a sliver of control over her life, and wanting to run away from all her troubles, if only for a couple of hours.

'OK,' she agreed, 'but only if you let me make you lunch. Danny will be hungry in half an hour, so we'll leave after we've eaten.'

'It's a deal. What are we having?'

'Just soup, I'm afraid, but it's homemade.'

'What flavour?'

'Lentil and vegetables. It's Danny's favourite. I make the bread myself too.'

'Ooh, homemade bread. How can I refuse? You're a woman of many talents.'

Another small smile. 'The bread maker does all the hard work; all I do is shove the ingredients in. Mum bought it for me for Christmas one year, after I'd complained that the price of a loaf of bread had gone up by five pence.'

'Your mum sounds like a thoughtful, practical lady.'

'She is. I think you'd like her. You'll have to meet her sometime.' She froze and he guessed what she was thinking – that meeting the parents was a great big step along the relationship road.

'I'd love to,' he said warmly. 'And you must meet mine, although they live in Kent now, so it won't be any time soon.'

He was suddenly glad he'd decided to return to the area he called home when he came back to the UK and hadn't bought a place near his mum and dad.

Very glad indeed.

Chapter 30

The oven still called to Edie, but she could see the sense in getting out of the cottage for a bit, if not for her sake, then for Danny's. She felt dreadful that she'd put him in such a position and seeing where James lived would be just the ticket to taking his mind off things.

Edie wasn't sure what she'd been expecting when James had said his house wasn't up to much. The Hopkins place had been empty for a couple of years, she knew, and James had warned her it was in a bit of a state. But his 'bit of a state' might have meant that it didn't have a Smeg fridge and a power shower.

He hadn't been lying, though. The drystone walls flanking the potholed track leading to the property looked to be in good repair, but the wooden gate lay drunkenly on the side, wedged open with a couple of substantial stones. The drive (if you could call it that) was full of ruts and holes, and she was forced to hang on to her door handle as the vehicle bumped and bounced along it, the suspension creaking in protest.

'It won't always be like this,' James promised, as he dodged around a particularly deep crater. 'But the house has to come first if I want to survive the winter.'

From the outside, his home looked perfectly habitable. The slate roof was free of the mould and moss that older roofs acquired, and seemed to be in good condition; the windows and the door were new, painted a deep green; and the pointing between the stones the house was built out of was fresh.

It was only when James opened the front door and ushered her and Danny inside that she realised what he meant.

It was a building site, and that was being kind to building sites! The walls were bare stone, which was fitting for the outside, but wasn't exactly warm and cosy for the inside; the floors were flagstones with footprints in the dust which lay thickly on top of them; one set, large, most likely belonging to James. A lightbulb, minus a fitting or a shade, dangled from a wire in the centre of the hall, and a couple of bags of rubble were stacked near the door.

'Nice place you've got here,' she said. 'Are you going for the rustic look?'

'Ha, ha, very funny. It's a work in progress.'

'So I see.'

'Come through to the living room.' He led her past a downstairs loo (please don't let me have to pee, she prayed silently when she spotted a toilet roll balanced on a brick and the absence of a loo seat), and turned a corner to reveal a wider hall which sported an impressive wooden staircase. There were another couple of doors, one of which she assumed must lead to a kitchen, and the living room at the far end.

As living rooms went, it was a decent size, running the width of the house, and had a dual aspect, plus a lovely old fireplace, which needed a bit of a clean; Edie itched to get her hands on a bucket of hot water and a scrubbing brush and get stuck in. With a bit of effort, it would come up a treat.

Danny ran ahead of her, darting into the room, but he soon pulled up. 'Whoa, where's your TV?' he asked, sounding aggrieved.

'I haven't got one.' James was smiling.

Danny's mouth dropped open. 'Are you sure?' he asked, as if he thought James might have one, but was hiding it. 'You've not got a sofa, either.'

The room contained two white plastic garden chairs and an upended crate, with an empty mug on it.

'Nope. No sofa. There's no point until I finish the building work, because it will only get dirty,' James explained.

The condition of the room was remarkably similar to the hallway – bare brick, bare floors, bare lightbulb.

'You've got beautiful views,' Edie said. Once this room was finished it would be lovely. 'I hope you're not going to rip that out,' she said, pointing to the fireplace. 'It's an original feature.'

'No, it's staying,' he said, 'although I am going to take part of this wall out and put in full-length doors. When they're in, I should be able to see right down the valley to Tanglewood.'

'Will I be able to wave to you from my bedroom window?' Danny asked.

'I doubt it. Your window faces the other way, and even if it didn't, I'd need binoculars to see you.' James then had to explain what binoculars were. 'I've got a pair in the truck,' he said. 'Go and fetch them, and I'll show you how to look through them.'

'What do you think?' James asked Edie as her son scampered out.

'It'll be lovely when it's done,' she said. 'Of course, I haven't seen the rest of it yet.'

'Go and explore, while I introduce Danny to bird-watching,' he said, and Edie couldn't resist. It was like being on the set of *Grand Designs* (another of her favourite TV shows).

On peeking through various doors downstairs, she discovered that besides the living room and a loo, there was a kitchen (badly equipped and very basic); another room leading off that to the outside which had a couple of pairs of Wellington boots in it and a waxed cotton jacket; a small room with a sink, which could possibly be used as a laundry room or a pantry; and two square rooms, half the size of the living room, which were totally empty. One of them would make a lovely dining room, although the kitchen was plenty big enough to hold a farmhouse table and six chairs.

Upstairs had a bathroom with an ancient stained bath, which had an odd contraption rigged above it, and a toilet (in better condition than the one downstairs), plus four bedrooms. It was easy to tell which one James was using because it was the only one which had a bed.

For a second, she had an image of James in it, but she pushed it away. Now definitely wasn't the time to be having lascivious thoughts, not when she had much more important matters on her mind, like what the hell she was going to do for money when she'd used the measly wages that Mrs C owed her.

Brought back to reality with a bump, she bolted back down the staircase to find James and Danny. Danny was balancing the binoculars on the windowsill and peering through them, James standing behind him. The sight of the two of them together gave her a pang. They looked like father and son, enjoying some quality time. The image was quite disconcerting.

This was what was missing from Danny's life, she realised: a positive male role model and influence. He'd spent too much time in her company or that of her mother's, surrounded by swathes of fabric and diamantes. He needed to be outside, grubbing about in the dirt, or playing footie, or—

'What do you think, now you've seen all of it?' James asked her, interrupting her thoughts.

'Are you doing it up to sell?'

'No, I intend to live in it.'

'It's a bit big for one person...'

'You think it needs a family?'

'Don't you?'

'Yes. In time.'

It was quite a large house – he'd rattle around in it all on his own. A sudden vision of children – James's children – running through the downstairs rooms popped into her mind, and she frowned.

'What?' he wanted to know.

'I'm surprised you haven't got an army of builders working on it right now,' she said.

'I wish! Apart from the stuff I've had to contract out because I'm not qualified, I've done all the work myself.'

He sounded immensely proud of the fact, and so he should be; he was doing a fine job. If she had his money, though, she'd not be knocking black plaster off the walls herself; she'd be thinking about where she'd be putting the furniture and watching someone else do the hard work. Still, some people gained a lot of satisfaction from doing things like this themselves, and James seemed to be one of them. She certainly didn't hold it against him – instead, she appreciated his work ethic.

'It'll take you years,' she pointed out.

He smiled cheerfully. 'Nah, it's watertight already, and over the next couple of months I'll have the electrics and the plumbing done, so at least I'll be warm going into the winter. As soon as that little lot is finished, it won't take long to nail the plasterboards on, and once that's done it'll start looking more like a home and less like a barn.' He stopped talking for a moment and looked at her.

'What?' she demanded.

'I wouldn't mind getting your input on the kitchen, though, and the bathroom. Like the sort of cupboards and the tiles...' He trailed off.

'I'd love to!' It would almost be like being in one of the renovation programmes she liked, except she would be advising someone else on how to spend their money rather than having to dig into her own shallow pockets.

'It'll be a while yet,' he warned.

Edie took a second to consider what he meant. Was he implying that he expected her to still be in his life when his house was ready for its new fixtures and fittings, or was he warning her that she might not be around?

Lordy, why were relationships so complicated? And were they actually in one?

'James is going to grow all his own vegetables,' Danny announced, the binoculars still firmly attached to his face, his mouth and nose scrunched up as he peered through the lenses.

'I've got a long way to go before the ground is ready to plant anything,' James said, with a laugh. 'In fact, I meant to ask if Danny would like to come with me to see a man about some goats?'

Edie raised an eyebrow. 'A man about some goats?' she repeated, deadpan.

'I'm not joking, honest. Goats are one of the most efficient and environmentally friendly ways of clearing all this rough growth.' He pointed to the patch of land to the rear of the house, and Edie peered through the window.

'It's chock-full of brambles and nettles,' she said.

'Goats will eat all that, and the thistles and the young rowan trees that are sprouting up. And after the goats, the pigs will move in.'

'Pigs?'

'To turn the soil over.'

'Of course. Why didn't I think of that?' Edie chuckled, then abruptly she remembered her own situation, and her chuckles died away. 'Thank you for taking my mind off things for a while,' she said. 'But I must get back.'

'To your oven?'

'To job hunting. I'd better take a look at some job sites and see what's out there. Not a lot, I expect, and definitely nothing in Tanglewood; or should I say, nothing that I'd be qualified for.'

'I wish I could help—'

'Thank you, but I can manage,' she was quick to tell him. There was no way she would accept charity from anyone, especially not from a man she'd not long met, no matter how much money he had in the bank. She valued her independence too much to be beholden to anyone. 'Danny, give James his binoculars back, there's a good boy.'

'He can borrow them—' James began, but she cut him off before he could say anything else. He'd already given Danny a rabbit (she still wasn't sure she believed the 'I found it' story) and had bought all the things Mary needed – she wasn't prepared for him to give her son a pair of binoculars under the guise of a long-term loan. She wasn't his responsibility, and she didn't want to give the impression that she was only interested in him because of his money. If she didn't knock this on the head now, there was no knowing what else he might think to give her. It might be out of the goodness of his heart, but it made her feel uncomfortable.

She led the way outside, leaving James to lock up, and clambered into the jeep without a word, her head full of worry and her heart full of dread, as she wondered how she would manage. She barely had enough left over for things like new school uniforms, the odd treat of a cake from the bakers, or taking Danny to the Summer Fete.

Then she paused as she was about to clamber up into the 4x4, realising that she had been overreacting. She would have certain rights regarding not being evicted because of her change in circumstances; plus, applying for benefits didn't necessarily mean too much of a reduction in her and Danny's standard of living because, let's face it, Mrs Carrington didn't pay more than the minimum wage anyway. She began to feel a bit of an idiot.

'I'm sorry,' she said when they were on their way, Danny unusually subdued in the back seat. 'I think I lost my sense of proportion earlier. It must have been the shock. If I have to claim benefits for the short term, I probably won't be much worse off financially. My only worry is that I'll be forced to take a job with long hours, or one I can't get to and from very easily, otherwise they might stop the payments.'

'Does that happen a lot?'

'I've read about it and seen it on the news, so maybe.'

'Perhaps you should contact Citizens' Advice – they should be able to tell you what's what.'

'Good idea. I'll give them a ring when I get home.'

Preoccupied again, she didn't invite James in this time, wanting to make some calls and wallow a bit more. Despite what she'd said to him, she was still feeling rather fragile and more than a little shell-shocked. Only a few hours ago she'd been happily sewing away, with nothing more important on her mind than whether she'd ask James to stay for supper, and now here she was, out of a job and feeling very sorry for herself.

She'd have to thank James later for being there for her, but right now all she wanted to do was lick her wounds and wonder what she was going to do with herself for the rest of her life.

Chapter 31

James wasn't sure whether he'd helped Edie or not. He'd taken her mind off her problems for a few minutes, but ultimately he'd not been able to solve them for her, and that was something he dearly wished he could do. The strain around her eyes, the hollows beneath them, and the tightness of her mouth, tugged at his heartstrings. The unfairness of it – the way bad things happened to good people – was particularly galling.

Not wanting to return home yet, even though he had so much to do that he didn't know where to start, he left Edie and Danny at their front door and wandered down the high street towards Peggy's Tea Shoppe. A slice of cake and a cuppa was calling to him, and without so much as a crumb at home, he'd simply have to pop in and treat himself.

He had considered suggesting to Edie that she and Danny should join him, but the expression on her face and the way she'd refused to let Danny have a loan of the binoculars made him change his mind. She obviously wasn't in the mood for socialising, and he didn't blame her. Besides, he wasn't sure his wallet was up to paying for cake and tea times three.

He grabbed a free table and sat down, before taking his phone out. Maybe he should call Tia and let her know what was going on? He knew how awful she felt about what had happened, but he wasn't sure what, if anything, he could tell her that would make her feel any better.

While he was dithering, Tia rang him.

'Well?' she demanded. 'How is she?'

'Not too good, I don't think, but trying to put a brave face on it.'

'I wish there was a job going up at The Manor, but until Julia gets the wedding business off the ground, she's operating with basic staff.'

'I'm sick to death of weddings,' James moaned, then spotted Betty, the elderly waitress, at his elbow, waiting to take his order. 'Oh, can I have a pot of tea and a slice of that marble cake, please?' he said to her, before returning to Tia. 'Sorry, I'm in Peggy's Tea Shoppe for some consolation cake to cheer me up.'

'Is Edie with you?'

'No, she wanted to go home, so I didn't ask her. I still can't believe Moira Carrington sacked her just like that. No warning, no nothing. I wonder if what she did is even legal.'

'Will she get any severance pay?'

'You're talking about Mrs Carrington, so I doubt it. She'll pay her what she owes her and nothing more. I wish I could do something to help, but for starters I'm not exactly rolling in it, and for another thing, I don't think she'd let me, even if I had the cash to help her out.'

'I've not yet paid her for the dress she's making for me, just a deposit, so she'll have that, which should help.'

'I suspect she'll use it to replenish the funds she used to buy the material in the first place,' James pointed out.

'Oh, I never thought of that. Of course, she wouldn't have been able to use the account Moira's would have with the wholesalers, would she?'

'Hardly, and thank goodness she had the sense not to, otherwise Mrs Carrington might have thrown the book at her and Edie could have been accused of theft. I know it's awful for her...' He glanced up to see Betty setting his pot of tea and all that went with it down on the table. Tucking his phone under his chin, he lifted the lid off the pot and gave it a stir, then continued, 'But I do think being sacked by that awful woman will be for the best. She treats Edie like dirt, pays her a pittance, and the poor girl works incredibly long hours. At least if she gets another job, she won't have to take her work home with her night after night. She reminds me of Cinderella!'

Tia was laughing. 'Dear God, do you seriously see yourself as her Prince Charming?'

'The pauper is a more accurate description,' James said wryly. 'Hang on a sec; can I help you?'

Betty had sat down at his table and was staring at him intently. 'Nope.'

'Then, why are you...?' He tilted his head and frowned.

'Don't do that, you look like an irate cocker spaniel.'

'Gee, thanks.' He turned his attention back to his phone. 'Sorry, I've got to go, one of the waitresses wants something.' He lowered his voice to a whisper. 'I'm not sure what.'

A laugh floated over the airwaves. 'Don't tell me, it's Betty, isn't it?'

'Uh, yeah.'

'She's a wise old bird, and if she's taken the time to talk to you, then she's probably going to tell you something worth listening to.'

'I'll speak to you later,' he said, shaking his head at Tia's comment.

'Now you look like a cocker spaniel with a flea in its ear,' the old lady said.

'Thank you, Betty.' He bit into his cake, determined not to let some batty old woman spoil his enjoyment of it.

'That girl of yours has got the sack, I heard,' Betty said.

'Where did you hear that?' James gave her a sharp look.

'Just now. You said so. What did she do?' Betty asked, her face alive with interest. 'No, don't tell me – I bet she was moonlighting.' She slapped a palm on the table. 'I'm right, aren't I?'

'How did you know? I mean, it's not as if she's done anything like it before.'

Betty tapped the side of her nose. 'I have my ways and means,' she said. 'Right, then, what are we going to do about it?'

'We?'

'Yes, we. There's a job going here. It's not much, but it's a start.'

'I'm sure Edie will think it's wonderful. I realise being a waitress isn't everyone's cup of tea, but people like yourselves provide a valuable service—'

'I was referring to the hours. *They* ain't much. The job is just fine.'

'Yes, it most definitely is,' James replied hastily, anxious not to cause offence. The way she'd said it, she'd given him the wrong impression and—

'Don't get on your high horse with me, young man,' Betty added. 'I'll put you over my knee and give you a good spanking.'

'That's not what I meant, I—'

'She's winding you up. Betty's good at that,' Stevie interjected, smiling as she passed his table.

'Oh, right…'

'Do you fancy giving little Edie Adams a job?' Betty asked her. 'She's been sacked by that stuffy cow Moira Carrington.'

'Erm, I don't know—' Stevie began.

'She wasn't caught stealing, or nothing. Moonlighting, that's what she was doing,' Betty explained, pinching a piece of James's cake and popping it in her mouth.

'Really? I… erm.' Stevie was nonplussed.

'You need another body. I can't do all this on my own, you know.' Betty chewed noisily. James saw her eyeing up the rest of his cake, and he hastily took a large bite before she polished any more off.

'I'm here,' Stevie pointed out. 'You don't do anything on your own.'

'It bloody feels like it, let me tell you. And with Cassandra not wanting to come back to work after having that baby of hers, we need all the help we can get. What if my arth-ur-itis starts to play up? Hmm? What are you going to do then?'

Stevie had a grin on her face. 'You don't have arthritis.'

Betty stuck her nose in the air and sniffed loudly. 'Just because I don't go whining about it every five minutes, don't mean to say I don't suffer from it.' She gripped her hip and moaned theatrically, while James looked on in amazement. 'Ooh, it pains me summat awful, it does.'

'It didn't stop you from balancing on a chair to reach the top of the cupboard earlier on,' Stevie said, giving him a conspiratorial wink.

'Well, it's hurting now. Probably because I had to get on the chair. Now, if we had some help, then she could do all the climbing about.'

'You needn't have climbed up there in the first place. You were just being nosey.' Stevie turned to James. 'I've made her a birthday cake and hidden it somewhere, but she insisted on hunting for it.' A pause. 'Do you know about Edie Adams?'

'Yes, I do.'

'Tell me what happened and I'll see about the job. Betty is right, we do need help, but it can't just be any old Tom, Dick, or Harry.'

'Edie *was* sacked, and she *was* moonlighting. But to be fair, she was only doing it to help Tia out.'

'Tia?' Stevie raised her eyebrows.

'Julia Ferris and that horrid Mrs Carrington tried to railroad Tia into wearing a wedding dress she didn't want to wear. Edie has been making another one for her on the quiet. But Mrs Carrington found out…'

'I asked Tia to be one of my bridesmaids, but she refused, which surprised me, considering I'm marrying her brother.' Stevie looked thoughtful. 'She doesn't seem to like the limelight much.'

'She's making up for it with the dress Edie has designed for her. I haven't seen it myself, but Tia tells me it's gorgeous and she's delighted with it.'

'Trust Julia to trample over everyone else's feelings – but I can't believe Moira Carrington fired Edie for it.'

'I can.' James's reply was grim. 'She treats her like dirt, like a bloody servant.'

'Jealous, that's what she is,' Betty piped up. 'Thinks she's better than the rest of us, too. I don't know where she's got them airs and graces from – she's worse than Julia Ferris. She was a waitress in a cocktail bar, you know. Edgar turned her into something new.'

Stevie barked out a laugh. 'She was a sales assistant in a department store, not a waitress. And that's a Human League song you're sort of quoting.'

'Wherever I hear it, I think of Lady-Muck Tonbridge,' Betty said.

'You listen to the Human League?' James asked, incredulously.

'You youngsters think you invented pop,' Betty grumbled. 'I was listening to that kind of stuff before you were born. Got the T-shirt to prove it.'

'Really?'

Betty sniffed. 'Don't sound so sodding surprised. I haven't always been this age, you know.'

Stevie rolled her eyes. 'Back to Edie Adams,' she said. 'Do you think she'd want to work here? I'd have to interview her, of course.'

James felt as though a weight had been lifted off his shoulders. This would be perfect for her; the hours would be decent enough, he guessed, it was right on her doorstep, and Stevie was a nice girl who was lovely to Betty. He hoped she'd be lovely to Edie, too.

James leapt to his feet. 'Can I tell her you have a job going, and that she's to come and see you?'

'Can she bake?' Stevie asked.

'I've no idea. She can make some mean soup.'

'Stop arsing about,' Betty said to Stevie. 'You and I do the baking anyway; Cassandra never did because she'd burn water. We don't need another baker; we need someone who can take the orders, mop the floors, and carry a plate or two without dropping them.' She turned to James. 'Go fetch her. Tell her there's a job here for her, if she wants it.'

James could have sworn it was Stevie who was the owner of Peggy's Tea Shoppe, not Betty, but in sudden doubt he looked at the younger woman for confirmation.

Stevie sighed and threw her hands in the air. 'What she said,' she cried. 'She's always bloody right, anyway!'

Chapter 32

Working in a tea shop was hard, but Edie didn't mind. She was used to hard work. What she wasn't used to was being on her feet all day. Sewing tended to be a more sedentary occupation, except when someone was being measured or had a fitting.

By the end of the first day, she was exhausted; her back ached, her arms ached, her head ached, and her feet throbbed. But she was extremely grateful that Stevie Taylor had seen fit to give her a chance.

When James had turned up at her door, less than half an hour after he'd dropped her off, to tell her that Stevie had offered her a job at Peggy's Tea Shoppe, Edie hadn't believed him at first. He'd had to practically drag her out of the house and march her across the road, a bewildered Danny trailing behind them, before she realised she was about to have an interview for a job she hadn't applied for, or hadn't known existed until two minutes ago, while wearing a pair of jeans and a hoodie, and not being at all prepared for it. Although how she was to prepare for an interview was beyond her, because she'd never had one in her life. Mrs Carrington hadn't interviewed her as such – she'd heard that Edie was fairly good at sewing and had asked her to take in the waistband of a skirt. That had been her interview.

Stevie's process had been much the same. The owner of Peggy's Tea Shoppe asked her a couple of non-threatening questions, then asked her when she could start, and they'd agreed a trial period of a week, and the following day Edie had begun work.

Despite it being physically hard, she found she was quite enjoying it. Her previous job had been a solitary one, unless sitting in on a consultation or when a bride was having a fitting. She'd usually spent most of her days in her ivory tower, aka the workroom, sometimes with hardly a word being exchanged between herself and Mrs Carrington, unless her employer was issuing instructions.

The easy and frequent banter between Stevie and Betty, and between those two and their customers, was going to take some getting used to. Edie didn't think she'd spoken so much in her whole life as she had today. And she had to do it all again tomorrow.

'Tell me,' Stevie said at the end of Edie's shift. 'What's Tia's dress like?'

Edie laughed and shook her head. She hadn't laughed so much before, either; the atmosphere in the tea shop was light and happy, and Edie loved it. Who knew going to work could be so much fun!

She mimed zipping her mouth shut. 'Oh no, I'm not saying a word. If you want to know, you'll have to ask Tia.'

'She did,' Betty chortled. 'Tia wouldn't tell her.'

'You thought I'd be a soft touch, did you?' Edie asked Stevie, grinning.

'The only reason I took you on was to get the low-down on Tia's dress.' Stevie gave a dramatic sigh.

'You'll just have to sack me, then, won't you,' Edie joked, 'because I'm not telling.'

'Spoilsport.'

'Do you want me to tell everyone about *your* dress?'

Stevie's eyes widened. 'Actually, now you mention it...' she began. 'What if it needs altering?'

Edie examined her critically. 'It shouldn't do. It fitted perfectly the last time you came in, but I suggest you pick it up from Moira's as soon as possible and if anything needs doing, I'll do it. I'd go and fetch it myself, but...'

'I understand, and thank you. I wouldn't want anyone else to touch it. Any idea who Moira's new seamstress will be, now you've left?'

'None at all. There aren't that many around. I don't mean to blow my own trumpet, but taking a hem up isn't in the same league as deconstructing a gown and putting it back together again. And I also design and make dresses from scratch.'

'Can you still do that? Design and make wedding dresses in your own time?'

Edie paused. 'James suggested the same thing, but I don't think I can.'

'He's besotted with you, that one is,' Betty piped up.

Edie's mouth dropped open. 'He *is*?' Then, more cautiously, 'How do you know?'

'You just have to look at the soft bugger. Anyway, I know stuff, and I know he thinks the world of you.'

Stevie gave Edie a nudge with her elbow. 'Do you *like him, like him*, or just like him?'

'Doesn't anyone have any privacy around here?' Edie asked, trying to sound stern and not succeeding.

'With Betty around? Not a chance.' Stevie gave the old lady a fond smile. 'She knows everything about everyone, even when she's not supposed to. I swear she's got a crystal ball tucked away in her sideboard.' Stevie put her arm around Betty and gave her a squeeze.

The affection between the two women was apparent, and Edie thought they behaved more like best friends than employer and employee. She could never in a million years imagine Moira Carrington treating her with anything more than icy disregard, and she suddenly realised that in dismissing her, Mrs C had done her a favour.

She was going to miss the wedding shop, because designing and making sumptuous dresses was in her blood, but she wasn't going to miss working for Mrs Carrington. In fact, now that Stevie had mentioned it, Edie did wonder how her former employer *was* going to manage without her. She wasn't so conceited that she considered herself indispensable, but she was astute enough to realise that Moira (ooh, she'd thought of Mrs C by her first name, and it made her feel quite daring) wasn't too keen on the nitty-gritty of her business. The woman enjoyed meeting her clients and going to trade fairs, and she presumably also enjoyed the book-keeping side of it because she'd always kept that close to her chest, but she didn't enjoy cleaning the windows, or putting the vacuum cleaner on, or making sure the loo smelled fresh. Moira also wasn't keen on opening the shop in the morning, preferring to appear when all the hard work had been done.

But more importantly, Moira Carrington couldn't sew. Not one stitch. Edie reckoned the woman would have employed a seamstress anyway, even if she had been able to do anything more than sew a button on, because Mrs C didn't like having to work. Which begged the question – who was she going to find to do what Edie had done, for the same meagre wages that she'd paid Edie?

No one, that's who.

Edie feared for Mrs Carrington's business. She'd have to outsource the alterations, which would cost money, and without a designer she could no longer attract customers by offering a bespoke dressmaking and design service. In fact, without Edie to make the gowns she'd designed, Mrs C would have to resort to selling off-the-peg dresses only, and because it was the custom design service which made her business stand out from the rest in the area, the shop wouldn't have the same appeal for brides who now had the whole of the internet at their disposal. Moira Carrington's unique selling point had just been sacked.

As she left her new place of work for the day, intending to pick Danny up from school, she wondered how long it would be before Mrs Carrington realised her situation and was forced to advertise for Edie's replacement. Making a mental note to keep an eye out in the local paper, she contemplated the very unlikely possibility of Moira forgiving her and asking her to come back, and if Mrs C did, how Edie might feel about it.

It was all pure speculation and rather silly to even think about it, but now that the idea had popped into her head she took the time to mull it over, before coming to the surprising conclusion that she didn't think she wanted to go back to the wedding shop. After just one shift working for Stevie, she felt lighter and happier than she'd done for years. Actually, she felt that way about everything, not only her job. She was beginning to feel that way about her love life.

And it was all down to a lovely man called James.

Chapter 33

'Well? How did it go?' James asked, after the obligatory chat with Danny about Mary and being dragged outside to her hutch for the boy to show him how well he was looking after the little creature.

'Brilliantly!' Edie cried.

He'd guessed she might have had a good day by the wide smile on her face when she'd opened the door to him.

'In that case, I think we should go out to dinner to celebrate, and you can tell me all about it,' he suggested.

'Um...'

'I was thinking about a fish and chip supper down by the river.'

'Oh, OK. That sounds good. Shall I bring an old blanket for us to sit on?'

James nodded, and she went upstairs to fetch one.

While he waited, he thought about her hesitation, thankful that she hadn't been expecting to go to a pub or a restaurant. He'd offered, so he intended to pay, but he was hoping to save his pennies to pay the electrician what he owed him. Once he'd done that, most of the big jobs, the ones he wasn't skilled enough or qualified to do, would be out of the way, and he could start putting the house back together. It was amazing how quickly the place would begin to come together once the plasterboard was on the walls. Of course, he still had the spendy problem of a fitted kitchen, an en-suite, the family bathroom and the downstairs loo to consider. Although he had used the time between waking up and going to work today to make a hole in the wall where the floor-length doors would go, so he was making progress, of sorts.

'Shall I bring a drink?' Edie wanted to know, appearing in the kitchen with a blanket draped over her arm.

'I've got a couple of bottles of sparkling apple juice in the car,' he said. 'I'll go and fetch them and we can pretend it's cider.'

'Talk about living the high life,' she joked.

Danny asked if they could take Mary with them. Edie was a little reluctant, telling him that she'd not risked taking the rabbit out of the house since the incident with the Dalmatians, but said she felt sorry for the bunny, and eventually agreed after he promised he'd be responsible for her and he'd not let her off her leash.

Early evenings along the river path were a mecca for dog walkers, joggers and families with children, so after they'd bought their fish and chip suppers, Edie led them across the field away from the main path, to where some large flat stones had been placed.

'We shouldn't be bothered too much over here,' she said, sitting on one of them, 'and Mary can have a hop around without me panicking that a dog might decide she'd make a nice snack.'

While they were eating, James found his gaze being drawn to her again and again. The sun glinted off her hair, highlighting the gold and silver strands, and the prolonged spell of warm weather had given her skin a light tan and brought out a smattering of freckles across her nose. Danny had the same freckles, and a surge of affection for the lad swept through him. The pair of them had the same colour eyes too, and similar expressions, and a tiny part of him was grateful that the boy didn't appear to have anything of his unknown father in him.

'Come on,' he said to Danny, after they'd licked the last of the vinegary saltiness off their fingers and washed their alfresco meal down with the apple juice. 'How about if we leave your mum in peace for a few minutes, and see if there are any sticklebacks in the river?'

Danny didn't need asking twice. He jumped to his feet and grabbed hold of James's hand, tugging him across the field.

James shot Edie a smile, and was rewarded by seeing her face light up; he marvelled at how relaxed and happy she looked. He wanted to ensure she stayed that way forever, and a feeling of intense protectiveness swept over him, so strong it almost made him catch his breath.

'Are you Mum's boyfriend?' Danny asked.

Lordy, nothing escaped this child, James thought. 'I'd like to think so.'

'You have to be, because you've been kissing.'

If only it were that simple. 'A kiss doesn't mean you're boyfriend and girlfriend,' James said, trying not to chuckle.

'It does! I kissed Mary Lewis and she's my girlfriend.'

Oh, the innocence of childhood. 'She is?' He glanced at Danny.

The boy nodded earnestly.

James scanned the riverbank, looking for an easy route down to the water. He didn't want Danny slipping in the mud. 'Mary, eh? She's got the same name as your rabbit.'

This time, when he looked at him, the child was blushing.

'Did you name your rabbit after your girlfriend?' James asked.

'No. Yes. I suppose. Except she wasn't my girlfriend then, and she is now.' He sent James a worried look. 'You won't tell my mum, will you?'

Oh, dear...

'I can't promise not to tell her,' James said, 'because there might come a time when I might have to.'

'Like when?'

'I don't know. Look,' James said, seeing Danny's stricken expression, 'how about if I don't say anything for now. I don't like keeping secrets from your mum, but as long as I can't see a problem with it, I'll not mention it to her. Deal?'

Danny considered it for a moment. 'Deal,' he agreed, his face brightening. 'And James?'

'Yes?'

'I really like you.'

'I really like you, too.' He ruffled the boy's hair.

'I think my mum really likes you.' Danny's face was open and guileless. 'Do you like her?'

'Very much.'

'Have you told her? I told Mary. That's why she kissed me.'

'No, sprout, I haven't.'

Danny's expression was earnest. 'You should. Because she won't know otherwise.'

Out of the mouths of babes...

Chapter 34

There were goats. Five of them. The three nannies and two half-grown kids were peering at Edie with undisguised curiosity, although their nosiness didn't prevent their jaws from working overtime as they munched on a particularly tall thicket of brambles and assorted nettles. Edie winced as she imagined the nasty sting the plants gave. Those goats must have mouths like old leather, even the youngsters, she thought, because they were happily tucking in, too.

'I like goats,' Danny announced. 'Can I give them names?'

'They already have names,' James said. 'One of them is called Deirdre, another is Mabel, and I think the third nanny goat is Pansy.'

'Which is which?'

'I haven't got a clue. But I bet you don't know that these goats are the very same ones in the Three Billy Goats Gruff story, who had to cross the bridge where the troll lived.'

James winked at Edie and she stifled a smile. He was very good with her son, who was currently eyeing him doubtfully.

'They aren't. Are they?'

'Yep. See their horns? That's what they used to knock the troll into the river.'

Danny wasn't convinced. 'But they have babies.'

'That's because they lived happily ever after. The troll didn't.'

'Thank you for taking him with you,' she said to James. James had picked Danny up and had taken him to the farm where the goats currently lived to arrange for them to be dropped off at James's place, and as soon as her shift in the tea shop had finished, James and Danny had collected her and brought her to the smallholding so she could see them, too.

'He's been a great help,' James said, though what it was that Danny had helped with, he didn't expand on. It was enough for her to see her son puff out his chest with pride at the praise.

'Do you know you can get milk from goats?' Danny informed her. 'It doesn't come just from cows. I don't think I'd like it,' he added, dubiously.

'The next time I go to the shop, I'll see if they have any, and if so, I'll get you some for you to try,' James promised. 'Do you think you can check the tether for me?'

'Mum, the big goat over there has a bell on her. She's the lead goat, and the others listen out for the bell and stay close enough to hear it. That's why only the lead goat needs to be tied up.'

'The tether is twenty feet long,' James said to her. 'But if she wasn't tied to it, she'd be jumping up on the drystone walls and be over the top like a—'

'Sure-footed goat?'

'Yeah.' His smile made her heart skip a beat. Especially when he looked at her the way he was doing now, as if he wanted to eat her all up.

She cleared her throat and turned away, deliberately breaking the mood. For now. She'd ask him to stay for supper when he dropped her off, and once Danny was safely tucked up in bed, they could rediscover that very same mood and—

'Mum, are you OK?' Danny had stopped what he was doing and was staring at her.

'Yes, I'm fine. Why?'

'You had a weird look on your face. I thought you were going to be sick.'

Charming! There she was, thinking about the way James made her feel, and her son thought she looked ill.

'Come into the house – there's something I want to show you,' James said.

Edie, after a quick check on Danny to make sure he was OK, followed James inside, then stopped in surprise.

The hall was no longer bare brick. It wasn't finished by any means, but it looked 100 per cent better than it had done. It was covered in plasterboard, making it appear lighter and more airy.

'My word!' she exclaimed.

'Go into the living room,' he urged, and she did as she was told, stopping once again when she set eyes on it. The French doors were now installed and the view down the valley was breathtaking.

'Oh, it's wonderful!'

Dragging her attention away with difficulty, she scanned the room. It, too, had a covering of board, hiding the bare brick, the electric trunking, and the pipes from the central heating. James had even cleaned the ceramic tiled fireplace and black-leaded the appropriate parts. As she'd originally thought, the room would be fantastic when it was done, and it was now over halfway there.

'What about the kitchen?' she asked.

'Ah, well, now that's not in such good a shape.'

'In what way? Oh, I see,' she said, as she stepped in through the door. There wasn't one. It was still in the same condition as it had been the last time she'd seen it, although James had also boarded the walls. There were simply no units.

'Any suggestions?' he asked.

'A decent cooker would be a start.'

'Silly! I meant for the units. To be honest, I've been to a couple of places, but the choice is overwhelming, and I've no idea what colour to go for or what style. I was hoping you could help. The only things I don't want to change are where the sink is, because all the plumbing is done, and where the oven will go.'

'Worktops,' Edie said, turning slowly around. 'The one thing I hate about my kitchen is that there's no space to prepare anything. You'll want a countertop running from here to here.' She held out her arms, to show what she meant. 'Cupboards here, and I suggest the fridge goes here, so—'

'Wait a sec. Let me grab some paper and a pen, and I'll sketch it out. So, you think a cupboard should go here, one here...'

She stood next to him, peering over his shoulder as he drew, his nearness making her feel giddy. Breathing in the scent of him, a clean, male smell mixed with the faint aroma of soap and washing powder, she felt her knees wobble and her tummy turn over, and she tried not to stare at his profile. The concentration on his face was quite endearing; the way he frowned slightly and bit his lip as he tried to visualise his new kitchen.

'How about the style?' he asked, leaning back to give her a decent view of his sketch. 'High tech gloss, or rustic wood?'

'High tech,' she began, then cleared her throat to persuade her voice to work properly and stop being so husky. 'High tech would be out of place, I think. I've never been a big fan of gloss – not if you want a family. Little hands can leave an awful lot of sticky fingerprints. As for rustic...' She was getting into her stride now, the problem of James's perfect kitchen going some way towards calming her fluttering emotions, and she picked up one of the brochures he'd acquired and flicked through it, searching for inspiration. 'The rustic would be too farmhouse. Yes, I know it *is* a farmhouse, but I think wood will be too dark, unless it's painted a nice, bright colour. I've got it; how about this one?'

She pointed to an ivory kitchen with simple shaker-style doors. 'With white tiles and a couple of copper pans, it would look bang up to date without being too industrial or loft conversion-ish.'

'Is this the kitchen you'd like to have?'

'Would I! It's gorgeous.'

'OK, then, decision made.'

'Wait, aren't you going to work out how much it'll cost?'

James shrugged. 'It will be what it will be. These are all more or less around the same price, and I've got to have a kitchen, especially if I want to cook for you in it.'

'You can cook?'

'I most certainly can. Don't sound so surprised. I'm pretty good, too, if you like simple stuff, like stir fry.'

'I'm surprised, because you never mentioned cooking before.'

He looked around his non-existent kitchen pointedly. 'I'm not even going to attempt to make you a meal in this mess,' he said, 'so I suppose the subject never came up.'

He grabbed her around the waist and pulled her into him. Automatically, she wrapped her arms around his neck, and breathed out a slow sigh of anticipation as she closed her eyes.

'Before I kiss you, there's something I want to tell you,' he said seriously.

Edie opened her eyes and stared at him. Please don't let him say he's got a girlfriend or something equally upsetting, she prayed.

'I really like you,' he said.

Edie froze. She certainly hadn't been expecting him to say anything like that.

'It might sound like the sort of thing an eight-year-old might say,' he continued, 'but that's because it is. Danny asked me if I really liked you, and I said I did: very much. He said I should tell you, so that's what I'm doing.' His mouth came closer, until his lips were almost touching hers. 'He said something else – he said you liked me, too. Do you?'

Edie closed her eyes again, and murmured, 'Yes, I do, very much indeed.'

'Thank goodness for that,' he whispered, then did what she'd been wanting him to do, and kissed her until she was breathless.

Chapter 35

Business for Sale

Fotheringham's is pleased to offer for sale a well-established bridal store, located in the exclusive Tanglewood area. The business has been built up over many years, and is offered on a freehold basis.

The property consists of three floors, the ground floor being the store itself, with the upper floors consisting of storage areas and a fully functioning workroom. Fixtures and fittings are included, along with all stock, and a healthy client list with ongoing sales.

The business has a fantastic reputation and a unique offering, as well as a friendly, personal service to all customers. With healthy financials and a prominent position in town, the business is set to grow if acquired by the right owner.

This is an excellent opportunity to purchase a thriving business in an affluent area.

Edie looked up from the advert, the newspaper rustling as her hands shook ever so slightly, to meet Stevie's level gaze.

'I thought it best to show you, rather than for you to hear it on the grapevine,' her employer said. 'I guessed you might be a bit upset. You worked there for years, didn't you?'

Edie nodded, not trusting herself to speak. Was it her fault that Mrs Carrington was selling up? She had a feeling it might be, and the realisation brought tears to her eyes.

Stevie patted her on the arm. 'I think the estate agent has taken a bit of a liberty, so God help the new owners. It's not exactly in a prominent position, is it?'

'I'm not sure that describing it as "thriving" is truly accurate, either,' Edie added in a small voice, grateful there was a lull in customers. She didn't want anyone witnessing her distress. 'I thought she might have a bit of trouble replacing me – not that I think I'm irreplaceable,' she said hastily, lest Stevie thought she was being big-headed. 'It's just I know what she pays, and most people wouldn't work for that.' She sighed. 'It's such a shame; she built the business up from scratch, but I could see that the bookings were dropping off even in the time I'd been there.'

'I think the advert is telling the truth, though. In the right hands, it could be a little goldmine.' Stevie smiled at her. 'In *your* hands.'

'Oh, I don't think so!' The very idea was preposterous.

'Don't be daft, young lady.' Betty wrinkled her nose at her. 'You can do anything you put your mind to, and don't let anyone tell you any different.'

'I think the bank might have something to say about that,' Edie said, mournfully. 'It doesn't mention a price, but I bet it's more than the measly amount in my account.'

'Get a loan,' the older woman replied, dismissing Edie's very valid objection with a wave of her liver-spotted hand.

If only it was that easy…

She bit her lip as a thought occurred to her. 'Please don't think I want to leave here, because I don't. I know it's only been a few days, but I love it, I really do.'

'You love sewing more,' Betty said bluntly. 'You're good at it, too. It's a pity to waste your talent.'

Yes, it was, she agreed silently, but there was no way she'd ever be able to afford to buy Moira's. Or anywhere else for that matter. Even the idea sent a shiver down her spine, although she had to admit that in the middle of those nights where she'd been unable to sleep, she had let her mind wander to some undefined year in the future when she owned her own bridal shop.

But it was a pipe dream, nothing more.

Since Mrs Carrington had sacked her, Edie had flirted with the idea of starting up her own business, despite what she'd said to James about it being a ridiculous idea. It still was ridiculous, as she'd been unable to see any way she could make it work, even as a cottage industry. She had the cottage, but no spare cash to use as start-up funds, and then there was that clause in the lease…

Despite loving her new job (it was Stevie and Betty who made it so enjoyable), she did miss sitting at her sewing machine, seeing a mound of fabric gradually transforming into a beautiful dress.

The bell above the door rang, and she stood up, folded the newspaper and left it on the table.

'Mrs George, what can I get you?' she asked brightly, seeing an elderly woman hobble into the tea shop, clutching her stick with white-knuckled hands.

'Are *you* working here now?' Mrs George demanded with a scowl.

'Er, yes, just started a couple of days ago.'

Mrs George ignored her. 'You never said there was a job going,' she said to Stevie. 'That job could have been mine.'

'Oh, shut your cake-hole, you daft bat.' Betty flicked a cloth over the nearest table, scattering crumbs onto the floor, and Edie hastened to fetch a brush. 'You're too old to be working.'

'I'm younger than you!' Mrs George looked furious.

'Only by two months. Pish!'

Edie swept up the crumbs and deposited them in the bin. While she was behind the counter, Stevie said out of the corner of her mouth, 'When I first opened and advertised for help, Mrs George applied for the job. But her idea of working was to sit at a table to take the orders and shout them across to me. And she couldn't work on Thursdays because that was her day for sitting in the doctor's surgery and having a chat, and she couldn't carry or fetch anything because of her leg. That's when I took Cassandra on.'

'And Betty?'

'Ah, now that's another story. Remember the floods last year?'

Edie nodded. The village had never seen the river so high, and the row of cottages down by the pretty hump-back bridge had flooded, along with the field that the Summer Fete had been held on.

'Well, Betty had nowhere to stay and I had a spare room, so she moved in with me for a few weeks. She insisted on giving me a hand in the shop in return, and it turned out that she's an excellent baker and an all-round good cook. She's a damned hard worker, too, so I gave her a job. Unfortunately, Mrs George has never forgiven her – she thinks I should have employed her instead.'

'I thought you worked in that wedding shop?' Mrs George called to Edie. 'It's lucky you found something else before she sold the place. The new owners mightn't have kept you on.'

Stevie smiled and rolled her eyes. 'That's one of the things I found hard when I first moved to Tanglewood – the way everyone knows everything. You can't keep a secret in a place like this.'

'That Moira Carrington did,' Mrs George shouted over the racket the coffee machine was making. 'I found out the other day that—'

'Hush your noise,' Betty interjected. 'There's no need to be spreading gossip.'

'Don't you tell me to shut up.' Mrs George banged the end of her walking stick on the floor. 'It's not gossip. I heard it from Archie Smith, who heard it from that woman who helps out in the antique shop when what's-her-name, who owns it, is out gallivanting with that married man who runs the newsagent in Abergavenny.'

Stevie muttered, 'See what I mean?'

'I suppose it does take a bit of getting used to,' Edie conceded. Not having lived anywhere else but Tanglewood, she was used to it. And talking of trying to keep secrets, her mother's neighbour had known Edie was pregnant before Edie herself had done. It had been a bit of a shock to both her and her mother when the woman next door had asked her mum over the garden fence if Edie was in the family way. That hadn't been one of Edie's better days…

'As I was saying,' Mrs George continued, 'that Moira Carrington is no better than the rest of us, despite her airs and graces. Thinks she's summat special, she does, but her shit smells the same as everyone else's.'

Edie grimaced. What a lovely turn of phrase to come out of a little old lady's mouth.

'There's no point in raking all this up. It happened years ago,' Betty warned.

'Yes, well, it's fresh enough for me, because I've only just found out about it,' Mrs George declared.

Betty glared at the woman, then stalked over to the coffee machine and blasted hot, frothy milk into a stainless-steel jug, the noise cutting Mrs George off for a moment.

When Betty flicked the lever to turn the milk off, she took a deep breath. 'If you're not going to keep your nose out of other people's business and you're determined to tell anyone daft enough to listen, then I think it's only right that folk should hear the truth, and not some nasty garbled version of it.'

'You're a fine one to talk about keeping your nose out of other people's business—'

'Be quiet!' Betty smacked her fist down on the counter, making Edie jump. 'Moira Carrington, for all those airs and graces you keep chuntering on about, hasn't had it easy. Her father was a vicar somewhere near Hay-on-Wye, and when she got herself pregnant without having a ring on her finger, he wasn't terribly happy about it. She was quite a few months gone, so when the bloke who knocked her up agreed to marry her, her father insisted on a small wedding done on the quick: no white dress, no reception to speak of, no fuss. It was the shame, you see. Then the vicar was even more ashamed when the poor girl was jilted at the altar. The father of her baby was seeing another lass, who he appeared to like better than Moira. Got *her* pregnant, too, a couple of months later, but at least he married that one. It might have been the shock, but Moira Carrington lost the baby and she's never been the same since. Became obsessed with weddings, she did. I suspect, as she didn't get to have her own, she got to experience it by proxy.'

Betty paused for a moment. No one spoke. Even Mrs George remained silent.

Eventually, Betty said, 'I would have thought she'd be more inclined to cut up wedding dresses, not sell them, given the circumstances, but there's no accounting for the weirdness of folk.'

Edie was flabbergasted. Poor Mrs Carrington. She would never in a million years have imagined that her former employer had such a tragic history. Although the story did go a long way towards explaining things, it still didn't excuse Moira's behaviour towards her. Or did it...?

'Do you know if she ever married or had children?' Edie asked into the silence.

Betty shrugged. 'Not to my knowledge.'

'That's so sad,' Stevie said.

'It don't give her the right to be so bloody awful to you,' Betty said to Edie, 'but I expect she might have seen something of herself in you. You're an unmarried mum, bringing up your son on your own after that good-for-nothing father of Danny's buggered off at the first sight of your big belly. That could have been Moira Carrington, if her child had lived.'

Edie sat down, the second shock of the day making her feel weak. 'She always seemed to dislike Danny. She didn't like me much, either.'

'Resentment, I'd say. Not dislike. She envied you.'

'*Me?*' Edie gave an incredulous laugh.

'You've got what she lost. A child.' Betty sat down next to her and placed a hand over Edie's.

'Why did she take me on, then, if she felt that way?' she cried.

'I don't know for certain, and I'm only surmising here, but I think there might have been two reasons. The most obvious is that you were desperate for work and could sew. The other is that she felt sorry for you.'

'She had a funny way of showing it,' Edie muttered. 'And I don't need anyone's pity or charity. I can manage just fine on my own.'

'My, my, aren't you the feisty one? That James Preece is going to have his work cut out with you,' Betty cackled. 'I wonder if he knows what he's letting himself in for? I thought Stevie with her ginger hair was fiery, but she's got nothing on you.'

'It's chestnut,' Stevie said. 'Not ginger.'

'Whatever you call it, it's still the same colour, ain't it? A rose by any other name…'

'Stop quoting Shakespeare at me,' Stevie muttered.

'What with you and Nick, Tia and William, Leanne and Rex, and now our little Edie and James, I'm torn between *Romeo and Juliet*, *A Comedy of Errors* and *Much Ado About Nothing*,' Betty retorted.

'How about *All's Well That Ends Well*?' Stevie asked, sending Edie a meaningful look.

Edie crossed her fingers and hoped it most certainly would.

Chapter 36

'Well, Tia, I hope you're pleased with yourself,' Julia Ferris announced over dinner.

James's attention was firmly on the delicious beef stroganoff, creamed potatoes and seasonal vegetables on his plate, but at Julia's tone he glanced up, wondering why she sounded so aggrieved with her son's fiancée.

He saw Tia take a deep breath before asking, 'Why, what have I done?'

'Moira Carrington is going out of business, thanks to your shenanigans.'

'Excuse me?' Tia narrowed her eyes at the woman under whose roof she was living, and who was soon to become her mother-in-law.

Although William was the next Lord Tonbridge and the roof was a jolly great big one, and William and Tia had their own wing, James did wonder how well the two women would get on in the long term. He realised the impending wedding wasn't helping matters, especially since the event was rather high profile and Julia was using it to showcase The Manor and the fledgling wedding venue business. Maybe the couple should forgo eating with Julia and Edgar, but as Julia frequently pointed out, it was silly for both families to cook separate meals when there was a chef on-site for the restaurant.

Personally, James was more than happy to be included in the family supper, but he could see how having Julia in such close proximity was getting on Tia's nerves, as this latest comment of Julia's proved.

'How have you come to the conclusion that I've put Moira Carrington out of business?' Tia asked, placing her knife and fork gently down on her plate, putting her elbows on the table and steepling them under her chin.

James had a feeling a battle was about to commence.

'By going behind her back and getting that needle-woman of hers to make you a dress. She's had to sack her, you know, for gross misconduct or something.'

James, swiftly eating the remainder of his meal in case he was forced to make a quick exit (he was *hungry*), watched Tia's eyes glitter, and her usually full and generous mouth become a straight, hard line.

'I was hoping to spare your feelings, Julia, and yes, I do blame myself; but if you hadn't ridden roughshod over my wishes and decided that you knew best, then I wouldn't have "gone behind her back", as you put it.'

Julia harrumphed, and shook her head. 'I was only trying to help—'

'No. What you were trying to do was to take control. As usual. And, as usual, I let you get on with it, because, frankly, it's easier that way. You've had your own way with everything regarding this wedding, from who to invite – believe me, I never wanted the Earl of Starkey to come to my wedding, especially since I don't know the man – to the filling in my wedding cake! But when I had a chance to think about it, I didn't want to wear that dress. I wanted to choose my own. So, that's what I did.'

'And look what damage that has done.' Julia pursed her lips.

James felt like he was a spectator in a tennis match, but with grenades being served, not fuzzy yellow balls.

'Edie Adams is far better off working for Stevie than she ever was working for Moira,' Tia declared. 'She's being paid a decent wage, for a start, and not having to work at home in the evenings in her own time. And Stevie doesn't talk to her like she's dirt, either.'

'It isn't Moira's staff I'm interested in. It's Moira herself. She's having to sell the business, and it's your fault.'

James sat up straight, a fork halfway to his mouth. 'What did you just say?'

'Moira's Wedding Shop is up for sale and you, my dear James, played a part in its demise, too. If you hadn't agreed to—'

'Hang on a sec. I was doing Tia a favour. Nothing more. I'm not taking the blame for this.' He dropped his fork on his plate with a clatter and stood up.

He knew Julia could be a bit high and mighty on occasion, but this was taking the biscuit. Besides, he'd done his fair share of feeling guilty when he'd learnt Edie had been sacked, but now that she was in a better paying job (not much better, but a bit), was able to work fewer hours, and was being treated like a valued member of staff and not like a servant, he didn't feel quite so bad about her situation or his small part in it.

'Sit down,' William said to him. 'Mum, give it a rest.'

'You know I prefer being called Mother. Mum is so common.' Julia lifted her chin, her nose in the air.

'I'll call you something else in a minute,' William muttered under his breath, earning himself a glare from his father.

Until now, Edgar, in his typical fashion, hadn't become involved in the discussion (or should James call it a squabble?) but it had the potential to turn ugly. James intended to leave before that happened and someone said something they'd regret. He had no intention of it being him, especially when his sympathies didn't lie with Moira Carrington and her uppity, rude, dismissive ways.

James remained standing for a moment, then, with William urging him to at least clear his plate before he stormed off, he sank back into his seat. It would be a shame not to eat the rest of his meal, because there wasn't a great deal in either his fridge or his freezer.

'Julia...' Edgar warned.

'I'm sorry, James, but you must see it from my point of view. Moira's Wedding Shop has been in Tanglewood for as long as I have. In fact, I was one of her first customers and bought my very own wedding dress from her. Of course, it had to be specially ordered from London. You've seen the photos, haven't you? No? I must show them to you; remind me. Anyway,' she drew a breath, 'that's beside the point. What I'm saying is that it will be a shame for it to close down.'

'I thought you said she was selling up?' William said.

'It'll amount to the same thing in the end. Who's going to buy a business like that in a little village like Tanglewood?'

'There must be loads of people out there who'd like to own and run a bridal shop,' William offered. 'I bet Edie would, for one.'

Julia harrumphed again. 'It's her fault Moira is having to sell. She can't get a dressmaker for love nor money.'

'Mrs Carrington is too short on love and too mean with money,' James pointed out, 'so I'm not surprised. Besides, it hasn't been all that long since she got rid of Edie. She's not given herself much of a chance to find a replacement.'

'You're right,' Tia said. 'I haven't seen an advert anywhere.'

'She might have placed one in her shop window,' Julia said.

'If that's the case, she's hardly likely to get much interest that way – she doesn't have any passing trade for a start.' Tia's face had lost the annoyed expression and was now looking thoughtful. 'I reckon she was probably planning on selling up anyway. What is she, sixty?'

'Actually, I believe she's closer to seventy,' Edgar said.

'There you go, then.' Tia nodded. 'I bet I'm right, and she was thinking of packing it in soon, anyway. But I'd never have guessed she's seventy. She's remarkably well-preserved.'

Julia sent her daughter-in-law-to-be a withering glance. 'That's the benefit of not having children. All the worry sends one grey and gives one wrinkles.' She patted her own immaculately styled and coloured hair, but the message was clear – her children (and their respective partners) were ageing her.

'Does Edie know that Moira's is up for sale?' William asked.

'I don't know,' James replied. 'This is the first I've heard of it, so maybe not.'

'Do you think she'll want to buy it?'

'Probably, but unlike you lot who are filthy rich she won't be able to afford it.'

Edgar chuckled. 'I wish. Land rich and cash poor, that's us. Why do you think Julia is opening the house up to weddings? Then there are the barns we're converting into cottages, and the residential crafting courses we're running. It's not easy keeping a place this size going.'

'Yeah, I feel sorry for you,' James joked, then stopped, his mind whirring. 'Wait a minute…' Everyone stared at him. 'I've had an idea…'

Chapter 37

Edie loved Sundays. They were lazy days, split between spending time with Danny and catching up on chores, and lately, seeing James. Today, however, he had someplace else to be, and the day stretched out before her, and for once, she wasn't sure what she was going to do with it.

She'd invited her mum for lunch, but Pauline had arranged to visit a garden centre in Hereford with the Tanglewood Gardening Club, and she was having a spot of lunch while she was out, so Edie decided to call in and see her later. Although her mum and James had got on like a house on fire the other day, when Edie had taken him to meet her, she wanted to have a catch-up, and see what her mother really thought of her man.

Her man! Ooh! It was strange, after all those years of being single, to have a guy she could call her own. Nice strange, that is. Thinking about him made her heart sing and brought a warm glow to her cheeks. She still couldn't believe he seemed to be as fond of her as she was of him, and she continually felt like pinching herself. Fond wasn't the right word, though. It was more than fond. Much more. And she was pretty certain he felt the same way, but when she tried to imagine what the future looked like with him in her life, she failed.

If they were to have a more formal relationship (was she thinking of marriage? *Really?*), how would that work? How would she fit into his privileged lifestyle? She had a feeling she'd be out of place, but the thought of being without him was too awful to bear. He'd wormed his way into her heart, and she couldn't cut him out of it without shredding it to pieces.

Anyway, she was getting ahead of herself (she had a tendency to do that more and more often these days, where James was concerned). He'd not mentioned the 'L' word, and neither had she. There was plenty of time for that, if their relationship continued to grow and deepen.

She heard her son talking to Mary and, wondering how to keep him occupied for the day, Edie performed her chores while Danny cleaned Mary's cage and gave the rabbit some breakfast. The day was going to be lovely, she saw, when she popped outside to give her window boxes a drink.

Edie had steadfastly tried not to look at Moira's Wedding Shop since Mrs Carrington had dismissed her (which was difficult since she lived opposite the shop and it seemed to glare at her every time she stepped through her front door), but today she couldn't help herself, curiosity getting the better of her.

The shop looked the same as it always did – elegant, expensive, exclusive, yet also pretty with the tubs of flowers outside. God, but she missed the place: the smell of the perfume Mrs C sprayed around the viewing area; the feel of silk, satin and taffeta; the gleam of diamantes, the shimmer of seed pearls, the sheen of lengths of champagne, ivory and brilliant white fabrics. She missed the quiet and serenity of her workroom, the steady chatter of the sewing machine, the whisper of her needle slipping into delicate material.

Giving herself a mental shake, she turned to go back indoors, when she noticed a piece of paper stuck to the inside of one of the windows. Knowing that Mrs Carrington wouldn't be in the shop on a Sunday – Edie wasn't sure if the woman had set foot in the place since the morning she'd sacked her – Edie darted across the cobbled courtyard and squinted at the notice.

She froze as she read it.

Then she read it again, her eyes searching the words for hidden meaning and finding none.

Someone had bought the shop.

Edie recognised Mrs Carrington's elaborate script-like writing (no printing out a typewritten sheet of paper for her), which thanked her clients for their support, and informed them that the business would soon be in the capable hands of the new owner.

She rocked back on her heels. Who was this new owner? How long before the sale went through? Did they have need of a dressmaker? And if they did, could she, in all conscience, turn her back on Stevie and Peggy's Tea Shoppe and all the friendship and support she'd been given to return to her former employment?

Slowly, she made her way back to her cottage, thinking furiously.

Stevie would understand, wouldn't she? But Edie did enjoy working at the tea shop, and the job had been a lifeline to her when she'd so desperately needed it.

'Can we take Mary for a walk?' Danny jerked her out of her confusion, and she had a thought. She desperately needed to talk to someone, so…

'Why not? Put her harness on her while I pick some flowers.' There were several gerberas in bloom, their colours vibrant and jewel-like, so Edie decided to pick a decent bunch, and then she found some stiff cream netting to wrap them in, securing the whole thing with a length of pink ribbon.

Not wanting to risk crushing the flowers by holding a wriggling rabbit, Edie asked Danny to carry his bunny himself until they reached the gate leading to the path by the river.

The cottages that had been flooded last year were just along the riverbank, and Edie headed for them, saying, 'I just need to drop these off, then we'll walk Mary in the meadow,' before coming to a halt at the last but one house, hoping she had the right one.

She did, she saw, when her knock brought Betty to the door.

'Can I pick your brains?' Edie asked, holding out the flowers.

Betty gave her a long look before taking the bunch and gesturing for her to come inside.

Edie hesitated. 'Do you mind if we chat out here? I've got Danny and his rabbit with me.'

'Bring them through. We'll sit in the garden. Just don't let the rabbit eat my lettuces. I've got enough trouble keeping the slugs at bay.'

Edie gestured to Danny, and the three of them followed Betty into her cottage.

'Oh, this is lovely,' Edie exclaimed as she looked around in delight.

'It wasn't so lovely last summer. Got flooded, I did. William Ferris and Nick Saunders spent hours sorting it out. I bloody hope the river stays put from now on. I'm keeping my fingers crossed that them beavers do their job, I'm too old for the upheaval.' She ran some water in the sink and placed the flowers in it. 'I'll put them in a vase later,' she said. 'I've just made a pot of tea. Want a cup?'

'Yes, please.'

'There's mugs over there. Bring one here and I'll pour. You don't take sugar, do you?'

Edie shook her head. 'Just milk, please.'

'Tell your lad he can have a glass of apple juice. There's a carton in the fridge.'

When they had their drinks, Danny carrying his very carefully out into the garden, Betty indicated they should sit down at a small wooden table with four folding chairs.

'I've not got much in the way of brains – they tend to shrivel as you get older – but you're welcome to pick them, for what it's worth,' she said.

'It's about Moira's,' Edie began, keeping a close eye on Danny and Mary as they explored Betty's very pretty garden.

'I thought as much. Though why you want my two penn'orth for, when you've already made up your mind, I don't know.'

'I've made my mind up?' That was news to Edie.

'Of course you have. It's a no brainer, as youngsters these days say.'

'It is?'

'You've come here hoping for my permission and to make you feel better about what you're going to do.'

Wow, Betty certainly did speak her mind. She'd known the old lady all her life, in the way that everyone knew everyone else in Tanglewood, but she'd not had much to do with her until she'd begun working in Peggy's Tea Shoppe. She was well aware of Betty's reputation for eccentricity, though, and for knowing things she had no business knowing.

'You're right,' she admitted. 'I have.'

'What do you want me to tell you? That you should follow your heart? To not let guilt and gratitude get in the way of what you want to do? To stay safe and never take a chance?'

'I don't know,' she said in a small voice.

'As I sees it, you've got two options. Stay put because it's easy and you feel grateful to Stevie for giving you a job. Or give it a go. The new owners might not take you on anyway, though they'd be fools not to.'

'Do you know who's bought it?'

Betty was silent for a moment. 'No,' she said eventually, but she said it in such a way that Edie thought the old lady wasn't being 100 per cent truthful.

'So, you're telling me I should go for it?' she clarified.

'Go for what?' Betty demanded. 'As far as I can see there isn't anything to go for yet. There's only that piddling little notice in the window saying the shop's been sold.'

'I could always pop my CV through the letterbox.'

Betty snorted. 'I wouldn't, if I was you.'

'Why ever not?'

'It won't do you any favours. Too clinical. And what if they asks Moira Carrington about you? Which they will do, if they've got any sense. She'll tell 'em she sacked you for stealing her clients.'

'I didn't exactly steal, and it was only the one. You make it sound like I was poaching business off her on a regular basis,' Edie objected, heat rising into her face. Betty was making the whole thing sound far worse, and far more calculated, than it actually was. There was no stealing – she'd been helping someone out, that's all—

'Oh.' The penny dropped and Edie's shoulders dropped along with it. 'It does sound bad, when you put it like that, doesn't it?' she conceded.

'And I've no doubt that's exactly how Moira Carrington will put it,' Betty said.

'I might as well not bother, then. No one in their right mind will employ me if I can't get a decent reference from Mrs C.'

'Stevie did,' Betty pointed out.

'Stevie's different. And you helped.'

Betty smiled, her face crinkling and creasing. 'I know what Moira's like, and Stevie knows you and Tia.'

'But the people who've bought Moira's won't know anything about me, or about the circumstances.'

'Then you'll just have to tell them, won't you?'

'How? I don't know who they are.'

'Post your CV through the letterbox, but add a letter explaining your experience and how you came to get the push. They'll either want to interview you, or they won't. What have you got to lose?'

'My dignity? I don't want to beg for a job.'

'You youngsters make me laugh. You want what you want, but you're not prepared to put yourselves out to get it. Anyway, it's not begging – it's making a sound business proposition. If they don't already have a dressmaker, then they're going to need one. You're doing them a favour by putting yourself forward.'

Betty certainly had a unique take on things; if Edie could convince herself that she wasn't begging for her old job back, but offering her services as a seamstress, then maybe she wouldn't feel so bad about it.

'Thank you,' she said, patting the old lady's hand. 'I'm going to take Danny and Mary for a walk, then I'm going to write that letter.'

'Good. Now, if that's all, I've got jam to make. I'm behind as it is.'

Edie picked up her mug and Danny's empty glass and took them into the kitchen.

'There's one thing you haven't thought of, my girl,' Betty said, as she showed her out.

'What's that?'

'You might not like the person who's bought the shop.'

'I'm sure I will. I get on with most people.'

'Yeah, well, you know the old Chinese proverb? Be careful what you wish for…'

Edie smiled as Betty closed the door. Anyone would be better than Moira Carrington.

Anyone!

Chapter 38

Edie didn't hear anything regarding the job at Moira's for several days, but just when she was about to give up all hope she received a phone call inviting her for an interview, and she had to sit down, her heart thumping so hard she thought she was having palpitations.

'Miss Adams? I'm calling on behalf of the new owner of Moira's. Are you able to attend an interview tomorrow morning at ten thirty?' The voice belonged to a woman, accent-less, well spoken, although Edie couldn't be certain of the age.

'An interview?' she squeaked. 'I... er... of course. Thank you.' She'd have to ask Stevie for an hour off, and she felt a bit of a heel even thinking about it, but Betty had been right, and she knew Stevie would understand.

'The short notice is unavoidable, I'm afraid,' the woman was saying. 'It's imperative that the business is back to normal as soon as possible, so apologies for that.'

When the call ended, Edie was shaking. An interview! Oh, my word. What was she supposed to wear? What was she supposed to *say*?

Edie had to tell Betty. She would have liked to speak to Stevie, but her employer was currently in Paris for a much-needed four-day break, and there was no way Edie would intrude.

'Betty, when we're a bit quieter, can I have a word?'

'I'll manage. It won't be for long, and if I get stuck, I can always rope old Mrs George in to help.' Betty's chuckle was full of mischief.

Edie narrowed her eyes at the old lady. 'How do you know?'

Betty smirked. 'I know all kinds of things.'

'Do you know who's bought it?'

'Ah, now, that would be telling.'

'You do know! I thought you did. Who is it? Are they from around here?'

Betty shot her a look out of the corner of her eye but remained silent.

'Or—' Edie was thinking. 'You don't actually know, but you want me to believe you do. Is that it?'

Betty tapped the side of her nose. 'That's for me to know and you to find out.'

'Oh, for goodness' sake!'

'Does it matter who's bought it?'

'Of course it does.'

'Why? You're determined to work there, no matter who owns it. And let's face it, if you can put up with Moira Uppity Carrington, you can put up with anything.'

Betty had a point, Edie conceded. If she was offered the job, she'd more than likely take it, although it did depend on the hours. If this new job didn't fit in around Danny, then she'd walk away. The hours she had been working for Mrs C were doable. The hours she was doing for Stevie were better. But no matter how much she missed her sewing, Danny's needs had to come first.

When the tea shop became less busy, Edie phoned James, feeling disappointed when he didn't answer, so she left a message. He was probably on the road, as she knew he'd gone down to London for the day. They hadn't planned to meet this evening, because he thought he might be back rather late, but she would have liked to have spoken to him.

Never mind, she'd catch up with him later.

'What did your young man say when you told him?' Betty asked her, as she placed an assortment of tiny cakes on a stand. This was a new thing, Edie had been told – afternoon tea. Consisting of a three-tiered stand of little sandwiches, bite-sized cakes and miniature scones with pots of cream, jam and fruit, it was going down a storm with tourists, cyclists and hikers. The occasional local had been known to indulge, too.

'I had to leave a message. He's gone to London today.'

'That's right, I did hear. A meeting with the Earl of Starkey, I believe.'

Eh? The Earl of Starkey? Edie hadn't heard James mention him, and she wondered how Betty knew about it.

'Who's he?' she asked.

'One of Edgar Ferris's cronies. Julia has invited loads of them to William's wedding; if they have a title, then they've had an invite. Sticks together like glue, that lot does, though the younger ones are a bit less set in their ways. Like royalty are. I remember old Queen Elizabeth – the Queen Mother, I mean, not Elizabeth the First; I'm not that sodding old – and how rigid the rules were back then. These new royals aren't so stuck-up. William Ferris is more like them. Normal. Ish. If you call being heir to that ruddy great big money pit called The Manor and being landed with a title when his father pops his clogs normal, that is.'

What was James set to inherit, Edie wondered. Did his father have a title? It had never occurred to her to ask, and a part of her didn't want to know. She preferred to think of James as ordinary, just like her. If his mother was anything like Julia Ferris, Edie thought she might run away. She wasn't brave like Tia, who, she knew, also hadn't been born into William's world. However, Tia did have the advantage of being Nick's sister. He, too, was at home with the aristocracy, and he'd competed against the likes of Zara Tindall, Princess Anne's daughter. So, Edie reasoned, Tia was used to that kind of life.

Edie wasn't. It was the one little niggle in her relationship with James. He might be wealthy, but that didn't bother her because he didn't flaunt it. But if he was destined to be a lord or an earl or something equally as scary, then she wasn't cut out for that kind of world.

Edie Adams didn't envy Tia Saunders one little bit.

Chapter 39

Should she wear something she'd made herself, Edie wondered, just in case Moira's new owner asked for a demonstration of her sewing ability?

Then she smiled at her silliness – Moira's wedding shop was stuffed full of evidence of her work. All she had to do was pick a dress at random from the rack in the stockroom, and the odds were that she would have designed it from scratch.

She'd be better off wearing a plain pair of black trousers and the cream blouse she'd bought in the sale last year. At the time, she hadn't the faintest idea why she'd bought it, but it had been reduced to almost nothing, and she'd fallen into the trap of not being able to leave it there for that price. She'd had some vague idea of jazzing it up a bit because it was rather office-y, but she'd never got around to it. At least it was finally getting an outing.

She laid her outfit across the bed, then got dressed in her usual workwear of jeans and a T-shirt. Even with an apron, she wasn't going to risk spilling anything over the blouse, so she intended to do a mad dash home to change before the interview.

She still couldn't believe she was being interviewed for a job she'd been doing for years. It was a little surreal, but she didn't have time to think about it because Peggy's

Tea Shoppe demanded her attention from the second she arrived until the moment she dashed out of the door, shouting to Betty that she'd be as quick as she possibly could.

Betty's vague 'Whatever' followed her out as she sprinted for home and the fastest change of clothes in the world.

Panting, she shot into her house and up the stairs, dragging her T-shirt over her head as she took them two at a time, then wishing she'd taken a tad more care, because now she'd have to fix her bun again.

Oh dear, she was in a right old tizzy as she checked the time. She had five minutes. *Five.* Arggh!

Kicking her shoes off, she struggled out of her jeans and pulled the trousers on, then shoved her arms into the sleeves of the blouse. In her haste, she realised that she was buttoning it up wrong, and had to start again, which she did, cursing under her breath.

Why, oh why, was she putting herself through this? She was perfectly happy at Stevie's. She didn't need this kind of stress in her life. If she carried on working at the tea shop, she could indulge her love for dressmaking in her own time. There was no need to swap one perfectly good job for another about which there were so many unknowns.

It didn't help that she hadn't had a chance to speak to James about it. She would have dearly loved to have had his input, but he'd called back when she was getting Danny ready for bed, and then when she'd rung him, he'd not answered. He'd sent her a message, though, saying he had every faith in her and that she was totally the right person for the job – which was sweet of him. His faith in her was touching, and she'd taken some strength from it.

A final check in the mirror (she still wasn't happy with her bun) and she was ready to go. Before she stepped out into the courtyard, she took a deep, steadying breath.

What was the worst that could happen? – They wouldn't offer her the job.

Would she be in a worse position than she was in now? – No.

She'd still have a job (one she liked, despite going for this interview), she'd still have a roof over her head, she'd still have a gorgeous, thoughtful man she was falling in love with—

Stop it – this was not what she should be thinking about right now. She should be focusing on a job she really wanted, one she was good at, and not thinking about falling in love with—

Stop it!

Get a grip and concentrate, she told herself, as she straightened her shoulders and marched over the cobbles.

You can do this, you can do this, you can do this…

Edie wondered if she should knock, or walk right in. Her hand hovered near the handle for a second, then she pushed the lever down, opened the door and stepped into the shop that she'd put her heart and soul into for the last six years.

James was sitting on the sofa with a huge grin on his face.

'What are you doing here?' she hissed. 'Go away. I'll call you later.'

'I wanted to surprise you.'

'You've succeeded, now *go*.' She cast about, craning her neck to try to see through the fitting room and into the office beyond. 'Where is she?' Edie whispered.

'Who?'

'The woman I'm meant to be having an interview with.'

'I suppose you could say that I'm her.'

Edie shook her head slightly. She adored this man, but she wished he'd disappear and let her get on with the interview. She was nervous enough as it was without her boyfriend turning up out of the blue. Why had the new owner let him in anyway, considering he was hardly there to buy a wedding dress…

James was staring at her, still grinning.

A little penny tinkled and turned in her mind before slowly dropping to her rarely-worn court shoes.

'You?' she said in a small voice.

He nodded. 'Me.'

'But why?'

His grin slipped a little. 'I know how much you loved your work, even if you didn't like Mrs Carrington much, so when I heard it was for sale, I—'

Anger flooded through her. How could he? What the hell did he think he was playing at? 'How dare you!'

'Excuse me?'

'I don't need your charity,' she snapped, more furious than she'd felt in a very long time.

James's mouth dropped open and his eyes were wide and full of bewilderment.

'I don't need your pity, or your sympathy, or your high-mindedness,' she ranted, not letting him get a word in. 'I don't need you to think you know what's best for me, and more importantly, I don't like people thinking they can buy me. I, mister, am not for sale!' And with that she stormed out of the shop, the little bell ringing madly as she slammed the door shut behind her.

She made it to the archway before she heard it tinkle again, and she guessed James was coming after her.

Whirling around, her hands on her hips, she yelled, 'Don't bother. Just. Don't. Bother. I never want to speak to you again!' The last word caught in her throat and she willed herself not to sob.

How dare he! She'd thought he cared for her, but he'd just made her feel like a rich man's mistress, having had the equivalent of an apartment bought for her. Except he'd probably realised that there was no way she'd ever accept anything like that from anyone, so he'd gone for her weakness and played on her love of sewing and her longing to run her own shop one day.

She wasn't looking where she was going, and hardly registered the beep of a horn as she stepped out in front of a car, forcing the driver to slam on his brakes and yell at her.

'Whatever,' she muttered back. If she'd done the same thing five minutes ago, she'd have been mortified, and extremely apologetic, but right now she couldn't care less about anyone else's feelings. He'd stopped in time, hadn't he, so what was the driver complaining about?

As she stomped across the road, her thoughts scurried around her head like rats in a maze. Had James bought the shop with the intention of giving it to her, and if that was the case, did she now own it? He'd better not have done, because if he had, she'd make him wish he'd never been born. Or had he bought it with the intention of letting Edie run it? She wasn't happy with that scenario, either. He'd be her boss, her employer, and that was just wrong.

Well, he'd have to find some other girl to run it for him, because she certainly wasn't going to. Either that, or he'd have to learn to sew pretty damned sharpish.

She dived into the tea shop, yanked her bag off her shoulder and headed into the kitchen to shove it on the nearest countertop. When she stomped back out again, the first person she saw was Betty.

'You could have damn well warned me,' she said. 'If I'd had any idea who'd bought Moira's then I wouldn't have made such a bloody fool of myself.'

'Is that what you did?'

'I don't want to talk about it,' she said.

'It's not too late to change your mind.'

Edie gave her a disbelieving look. 'Is that the kind of person you take me for?' she demanded, tears pricking her eyes and threatening to spill over and trickle down her hot face.

Betty gave her an odd look and was about to say something, but the old lady had been rushed off her feet in the fifteen or so minutes that Edie had been away from the tea shop, and the place was heaving with customers. There were orders to take, serving to be done, and tables that needed to be cleared. Betty had work to do, and so did Edie. She'd just have to push her shock and heartbreak to the back of her mind as best she could, and get on with what she was paid to do.

She'd have plenty of time to cry later, in the privacy of her own home.

But there was someone else to consider, someone who'd be equally as hurt by James no longer being in their lives – Danny.

Chapter 40

Now that the summer holidays were here, Danny attended the playscheme for a couple of weeks, to give his mum a break. Today they'd gone on a trip to Cadbury World and wouldn't be back until later, so Edie had an hour to herself before she collected her son. She would have liked to have spent it wallowing in misery while lying on her bed clutching a glass of wine.

Instead, she had to prepare a meal for a child who'd probably arrive home buzzing from too much excitement and sugar, and who'd be tired and grumpy to go with it as a result of a long and busy day.

While chopping vegetables and grilling chicken, Edie's mind kept returning to James and what he'd done. She'd been able to kind of ignore it up to a point while at work, because with only her and Betty to man the tea shop, she'd barely had time to think of anything other than the next order. Even when it had quietened down a bit, as it tended to do near to closing, there was still so much to do in the form of cleaning and preparing for the next day. She'd felt bad leaving Betty to a pile of baking, but Betty had shooed her out of the door, telling her to 'go home and get your head straight'.

So that's what she'd done: gone home, at least. Getting her head straight was an altogether different matter, and one which would require a great deal of time and fortitude. Damn it, but she had started to care for the guy. She'd even admitted to herself earlier today that she loved him.

Now look at her. A snivelling ball of wretchedness, who couldn't blame the tears trickling down her cheeks on the onion she was butchering.

Why had she let her guard down and allowed herself to be hurt? She should have kept him at arm's length – they could have been friends – but he'd chipped away at her like one of the walls in his farmhouse, until her defences had broken and she'd let him into her heart.

She was broken now, all right. Heartbroken. How could he do that to her? Treat her like something he could own if he threw enough money at her? There were women out there like that, she knew, but she wasn't one of them, and it hurt her to think he believed she was. His money, his title (assuming he had one), his position in society, meant nothing to her. She'd liked (*loved*) him for his down-to-earth manner and his ordinariness, but then he'd gone and spoilt it all by doing something Julia Ferris would do – riding roughshod over people's feelings and wishes. He had treated her the same as Julia had treated Tia, and Edie didn't appreciate it.

Now she was getting angry again. Good. It was infinitely better than this feeling of desolation.

Time to collect Danny. Time to put a brave face on things, and not let her son see how upset she was.

'I sat by Jack on the bus. He's got a new daddy,' Danny announced as soon as he saw her. 'I told him I had a new daddy, too.'

265

Oh, no… She blinked back tears, desperate for them not to fall. 'James isn't your daddy, Dan.'

'I know he isn't, not my real daddy, but he could be my new daddy. Like Jack. Jack's had three new daddies,' Dan added. 'I don't need three. Just James.'

Did he have to do this right now? If Danny had said this yesterday, she'd have been cautious but optimistic. But today, all he was doing was driving a knife through her already shattered heart.

How the hell was she going to tell him that he wouldn't be seeing James again?

She waited until he'd eaten (Edie had pushed her food around her plate) and the excitement of the day had given way to yawns and relative calm, before she broached the subject.

'You know you were asking me about James earlier?' she began, although he hadn't been asking, he'd been telling her.

Danny nodded, his attention more on the cartoon on the TV than on her.

'He's not going to be your new daddy,' she said gently.

'Why not? If Jack can have a new daddy—'

'Daddies are for keeps, like mummies. You don't get to have a new one every few months.' Her tone was rather sharper than she'd meant it to be, but honestly! Jack's mother swapped boyfriends the way busybodies swapped gossip. It wasn't fair for Jack's mum to introduce the child to every new bloke in her life, but that was the way she'd chosen to do things. Edie wished she'd not done the very same thing herself, although to be fair, Danny had met James as part of his mum's job, not because she'd been dating him.

266

Still, she should have known better. The number of times she'd sighed when Danny had told her about Jack's mother's latest fella.

'But James is for keeps,' Danny said.

Yeah, that hope had been in her mind, too…

'Dan, I… um… we probably won't be seeing much of James from now on; he's very busy and, to be honest, I don't think he'll be able to visit us—'

'That's not fair! He really likes me, he said so. I want to see him, and if you like someone then you should spend time with them.'

She couldn't argue with Danny's logic, but neither could she tell him the reason he wasn't going to see James again. How could an eight-year-old be expected to understand the complexities of an adult relationship?

She didn't want him to think that James had simply abandoned him, either. James might have been a high-handed idiot where she was concerned, but she had no doubts that he genuinely cared for her son. But what other option did she have?

'Can I phone him? Please? I'll tell him he doesn't have to take me out or anything. He can just come over for a little bit. I'll be good, I promise.'

Tears gathered, stinging and hot, and she felt like the worst mother in the world. How had she allowed them to get into this position? It was her fault that Danny felt he had to beg to see James. If she hadn't let attraction overcome common sense, then none of this would have happened.

'I'm sorry, sweetie, but we can't see James if he's not going to be around, can we?'

Danny's face crumpled and he began to cry. 'He can be around, if we ask him. He likes us – he *said* so.'

'Oh, poppet...'

She didn't think she could hurt this much, but seeing her little boy's heart breaking was shredding her own into little pieces, and she enfolded him in her arms, pulling him onto her lap, rocking him like she'd done when he was little, and cried along with him.

'See, Mummy,' he hiccupped. 'You want to see him, too. Please, Mummy, phone him and tell him we'll miss him. Tell him you really like him.'

I've already told him, she thought.

It took her quite some time to calm Danny down, but when he was finally settled on the sofa watching TV, his little face still red and tear-stained, Edie took herself off upstairs to have a good cry in private, while she sorted out the laundry basket. Her heart was in two, but the mundane things like making sure Danny had clean socks still had to be done.

She didn't hear the knock at the door, but she did hear a male voice and Danny's higher-pitched reply. As she dashed out of her bedroom, her first thought was that it was James, and her stomach lurched.

It wasn't.

The man looked vaguely familiar, and it took her a moment to think where from.

When she remembered, her stomach lurched again, but not in a pleasant way, and she felt sick. He worked for Eastern Estates, the company who owned her cottage.

'Danny? You know you're not supposed to answer the door,' she said, hurrying down the last couple of steps, worry making her sound harsher than she intended.

Danny turned to look at her, and his lip wobbled. 'You're mean,' he told her, then he whirled around, barged past her and stormed into the living room.

As he shouldered the door open, Mary hopped out.

Seeing the front door was wide open, she made a dash for it, hopping through Edie's legs and dodging around the man from Eastern Estates.

'Mary!' Danny cried, running back into the little hall. He, too, tried to dodge around the man on the doorstep, but Edie caught him around the waist and pulled him back. 'Get some carrot,' she instructed. 'We'll stand a better chance of catching her.'

'This rabbit is yours, I take it,' the man said.

'Yes. Danny, hurry. I can see her; she's tucking into the asters in the tubs outside the wedding shop.'

'I'm Gareth Fortune,' the man said. 'From Eastern Estates? I'm to give you this. Please read it carefully. I shall return next week to ensure your compliance.'

'Yes, OK, put it there,' she said to him distractedly, jerking her head at the narrow table underneath the row of coat hooks. 'Danny, you'd better go ahead of me. If you hold out your hand and call to her, she might come to you the way she did at the rabbit race.'

'Miss Adams, you *are* aware that it's contravening the terms of your lease to have a pet?'

'I know. Look, please don't move, not until we've caught Mary. I don't want her running onto the street.'

'Miss Adams—'

'Let me just catch the rabbit, then you can say what you've come to say,' Edie hissed over her shoulder as she followed Danny slowly across the cobbles. She didn't want to alarm Mary and scare her into running through the arch.

Edie angled herself towards the entrance to the courtyard, hoping that if Mary was spooked and made a run for it, then she stood a chance of heading the bunny off – although she knew from past experience just how fast the little creature could move.

Danny crept slowly towards Mary, calling her name softly, his hand extended. The rabbit's ears twitched, but she otherwise ignored him and carried on destroying the flowers.

Edie held her breath. He took a pace closer, then another. One slow pace after another, he moved nearer to the rabbit, until he was within touching distance. Edie thought Danny might have made a lunge for Mary, but he didn't. Instead, he crouched down, shuffled closer, and offered her the carrot. When the bunny stopped nibbling on the flowers long enough to investigate the treat, Danny gently picked her up and cradled her in his arms.

Edie's breath came out in a whoosh of relief.

Then she remembered the man on her doorstep, and she inhaled sharply again.

Squaring her shoulders, she returned to the cottage, Danny following. 'Put Mary in her hutch,' she said to him. 'I need to speak to Mr…?'

'Fortune,' the man reminded her helpfully. 'As I was saying, it has come to our attention that in direct contravention of the terms of your lease, you have a pet on the premises: namely, a rabbit.' He was looking at her as if he expected her to deny it, despite seeing the animal with his own eyes. 'Is that rabbit yours?'

'She's mine,' Danny said. 'Her name is Mary.' His little voice was both proud and defiant at the same time.

'Dan, put Mary in her hutch.' Edie was barely controlling her anguish. For the briefest of seconds, a thought had popped into her head that she could feed Mr Fortune a line that they were only looking after the rabbit for a friend who was on holiday and that it would be returning to its rightful owner shortly – but Danny had scuppered that idea.

'I suspected as much,' Mr Fortune said. 'Please read the letter. It explains our legal position and yours. You have one week to comply, otherwise Eastern Estates will have no choice but to serve you an eviction notice. I will return to inspect the property at the same time next week.'

'Mum, what does he mean, "eviction notice"?'

'Danny, please, just do as you're told and take Mary into the yard.' She'd have to tell him soon, but not right now. Not today, when she'd already broken the news that James was out of their lives.

'Look,' Mr Fortune said, his voice softening. 'I like animals. I've got a cat of my own. But you can't keep the rabbit here. I'm sorry. Good luck with rehoming it.'

'Mum?' Danny sounded panicked. 'What's he talking about? Why can't we keep my rabbit?'

'Thank you, Mr Fortune. I shall ensure the rabbit is gone by your next visit,' Edie said formally, then closed the door on him, leaning back against it as the strength drained from her body.

'Mum?' Danny's eyes were wide with fear, and her heart went out to him.

Please, no. He didn't deserve this, her sweet, innocent, trusting son.

'I'm so sorry, sweetie, but we're going to have to find somewhere else for Mary to live. Remember I told you that Eastern Estates, the people who own our house, said we can't have a pet?'

He nodded, his gaze searching her face.

'They say we can't keep Mary.'

'No. Uh uh.' He backed away from her, shaking his head. 'We live here. It's our house. No one can tell us what to do in our house.'

'We might live here, darling, but we don't own it. Eastern Estates have said we can live here, but we have to abide by their rules. And one of their rules says that we can't have pets.'

'That's a stupid rule.' He was clutching Mary so hard that the rabbit squirmed furiously.

'Be careful you don't hurt her,' Edie warned.

Danny's expression was closed and hard. He hadn't broken down in tears the way she'd thought he would, although she could see they weren't far from the surface. 'You need to tell them – she can't live anywhere else. She's mine, and I love her.'

'It won't do any good,' she said, her heart raw and bleeding at his distress.

'We'll live somewhere else,' he said.

'That's not an option right now,' she began, but Danny didn't let her finish explaining.

'I bet James could make them let me keep Mary. James can do anything.' And with that, Danny turned on his heel and marched into the kitchen.

Edie gulped back tears. Poor, poor Danny. Could this day get any worse?

Chapter 41

'What did I do, Tia? I don't understand. She said she never wants to see me again,' James said, rubbing his hands across his face, and feeling the rasp of stubble on his cheeks.

'You mentioned that on the phone. Tell me exactly what happened.' Tia offered him a cup of tea from the pot sitting on the patio table. She was under the shade of a wide umbrella with her laptop open in front of her.

James would have preferred something much stronger than tea, and lots of it. 'I don't want to disturb you when you're working,' he said.

'Don't be so silly. You're here now. Sit down, have a cup of tea, and tell me what's going on. I'm only updating The Manor's website. I can do that later.'

James sat, picked up the fine bone china cup, and noticed that his hand was shaking. He put the cup back down again.

'I was waiting for her in the wedding shop when she came for the interview. I'd persuaded Julia to let me tell her the good news, but Edie took one look at me, started yelling and stormed out.'

'And you've no idea why?'

He shook his head, miserably. 'She said she didn't need my charity and that she isn't for sale.'

'Pardon?'

'Exactly. It doesn't make sense. I was only trying to help, and I thought she'd jump at the chance; I know Julia isn't the easiest person in the world – and you should know – but Edie would be in sole charge of the day-to-day running of it. Julia wouldn't interfere. Much.'

'I'm glad you added the "much" on the end, although Julia doesn't know enough about wedding shop retailing to stick her oar in, and I'm sure Edie could handle her. Underneath your girlfriend's soft exterior, there's a sliver of steel.'

'I'm pretty sure she isn't my girlfriend any longer.'

'I wonder what got her back up. And what did she mean when she said she isn't for sale?'

'I've been puzzling over that. Maybe she thinks Julia's going to pay her a pittance, like Moira did?'

Tia frowned. 'I don't think that's it… Is it the thought of working for Julia that put her off? What did she say, when you told her?'

'I didn't tell her. She never gave me a chance.'

'Strange.' Tia poured herself another cup of tea. 'Do you want me to have a word?'

'I don't know if it would do any good.'

'I can only try. What have you got to lose?'

James, sitting there in the early evening sun, thought he might have already lost it. Right now, he felt numb, the realisation that Edie had broken off all contact with him having not fully sunk in. He had a terrible feeling that when it did, it would hurt worse than anything he'd experienced before.

She'd sneaked under his skin so gently that he hadn't been aware she was there until it was too late. He was smitten.

But the question was, should he ignore her comment that she didn't want to see him again?

He had to talk to her – he simply had to try again. And if she told him to go away, then so be it. At least he'd have tried.

Chapter 42

'I've run your bath,' Edie shouted down the stairs. She went into Danny's bedroom to fetch some clean pyjamas, listening for the sound of his feet dragging up the stairs.

She knew she'd have a hell of a job to get him to bed this evening; he was still so terribly upset at having to give Mary away, and at times he'd been almost inconsolable.

Anger at Eastern Estates bubbled deep in her chest, and she wanted to scream at the unfairness of it. She'd read the letter twice, then ripped it into shreds and shoved it in the bin, but not before she understood the effects of her 'non-compliance' and 'any continued breach of your tenancy agreement'. In other words, she and Danny would be served an eviction notice if Mary remained.

She briefly wondered whether it would do any good giving them a call in the morning and asking if they would reconsider, as long as Mary remained firmly outside and in her hutch. It probably wouldn't, but she was willing to try anything. The look on Danny's face after he'd realised that Mary had to go, on top of the news that he wouldn't be seeing much (anything, actually) of James, had broken her heart. He'd been in tears ever since, and only now had she managed to calm him down enough to try putting him to bed. Although she suspected he'd probably crawl into her bed at some point in the night, the way he used to when he was little.

'Danny,' she called again. 'Come and have a bath.'

The TV was still blaring out a Disney Channel programme. It was rather on the loud side, and she feared for his hearing. He'd go deaf if he carried on like that.

Sighing, she made her way downstairs to fetch him.

He wasn't in the living room, so she turned the TV off and poked her head around the kitchen door.

He wasn't there, either.

Aw, bless him – he must be outside with Mary, and she didn't blame him for wanting to spend every moment he could with his pet. The rabbit would be gone soon enough. It would make it even harder for him to say goodbye, but she couldn't deny him a last cuddle this evening.

She decided to go out to join him, because she'd become quite fond of the little creature too.

However, Danny wasn't in the yard. And neither was Mary in her hutch.

Worry nibbled at her.

Where was he?

She knew he wasn't in his bedroom because she'd just come from there, and she hadn't noticed him in the bath-room, which she undoubtedly would have done when she walked past. The only other place was her bedroom—

There was a piece of paper on the hall table which hadn't been there earlier.

The nibbling worry turned into a gnawing fear.

She recognised the handwriting, big and sprawling, written in crayon.

gone to give mary to Jams he will loook atfer her

'Danny!' Edie yelled, yanking the front door open, racing into the courtyard and out through the arch, to look up and down the road. The high street was far less busy in the evening than it was during the day, and she could see that he wasn't anywhere along it.

'Danny!' she screeched, turning this way and that, craning her neck. Fear, sharp and insistent, stabbed at her and she gasped with the force of it. Dear God, he was only little, James lived a good couple of miles away, and it was getting dark. She wasn't even sure that he knew how to get there.

What if he got lost, and was wandering about in the dark, frightened? What if someone abducted him? A boy leading a snow-white rabbit was bound to attract attention – the *wrong* kind of attention.

She needed to phone the police. James, too, and warn him to look out for Danny.

If anything happened to her son... Edie didn't complete the thought. She was too terrified to.

The police said they'd send someone straight round, and that she was to wait in the house in case he returned home. But how could she do that, knowing Danny was out there wandering the roads and with twilight descending rapidly? He wasn't going to come back, she knew. He was going to James's house, as his note said, and knowing how determined Danny could be when he had his mind set on something, she knew he'd keep going until he got there. Or until...

She couldn't think like that, so she ignored the advice from the police, grabbed her phone and some money, and headed out into the growing darkness in search of her son.

Striding along the high street (thank God James lived in the opposite direction to the river), she phoned him.

'It's me,' she said as soon as he answered, cutting across his cautiously delighted, 'Edie, I'm so pleased you called.'

'Have you seen Danny?' she demanded.

'Er… no. Should I have?'

'He's on his way to your house.'

'Mine? OK…'

'He's on his own and he's on foot. He's got Mary with him.' Edie was panting hard, and she was finding it difficult to hold a conversation and jog at the same time. Realising she wouldn't be able to keep this up for much longer, she slowed to a fast walk.

'*On his own?* But why?'

She stifled a sob. 'We've got to get rid of Mary. He's upset, so he's bringing her to you.'

'Right. I'll get in the car. How long ago did he leave?'

'Fifteen minutes. Twenty at the most.' Thank you, thank you, thank you. Despite what she'd said to him earlier, he'd not hesitated to offer his help, and for that she was truly grateful.

'Where are you?' he asked.

'Just outside Tanglewood, on the main road.'

'You keep walking, and I'll drive to meet you. When you find him, give me a call. He can't have gone far, not with Mary hopping about on the end of a lead, so the odds are he's only a short distance ahead of you.'

This time she did let out a small sob. He'd not said 'if', he'd said 'when', as if finding Danny was a certainty, and that was something else she was grateful to James for.

But Danny wasn't a short distance ahead of her, and it wasn't her who found him. It was James.

When a large car pulled over on the other side of the road and flashed its lights at her, she knew it was James and, peering out of the window, his face pinched and pale, was Danny.

Edie's legs almost gave way with relief, but a desperate urge to hold her boy in her arms overcame her weak knees and she dashed across the road, flung open the car, and scooped Danny into an awkward hug, almost strangling him with his seat belt.

'Don't you ever, ever, ever do that to me again, do you hear! Anything could have happened to you. Anything.' And with that she burst into tears.

'Get in. I'll take you home,' James said.

Not willing to let go of her son for a second, Edie unclipped Danny's seat belt and took him into the back with her.

The police were waiting for her when James pulled up by the archway. Edie scrambled out of the car, still holding Danny, who was in turn holding Mary. They must have looked a sight, and one of the officers narrowed his eyes and shook his head slightly.

'When you said your son had a rabbit with him, we assumed it was a toy one, not a real live one,' the officer said.

'Her name is Mary and she's mine, but a nasty man says I can't keep her,' Danny said.

Edie saw the police officers share a look, then glance at James. 'It's not what you think. Having a pet is against my tenancy agreement; my landlord says I have to get rid of her.'

'Is this gentleman your landlord?' the female officer asked. She hardly looked much older than Danny.

'No. He's a… friend. Danny was on the way to see him, to ask him if he'd have Mary.'

'Mary?'

'The rabbit.'

'Ah. Well, as long as the boy is safe and sound, that's the main thing. Now then, my young fella, you won't be scaring your mum like that again, will you?'

Danny hung his head. 'No.'

'Glad to hear it. Be a good boy for your mum. Goodnight, Miss Adams, and I'll ask in the station if anyone wants a rabbit.'

'Thank you, and we're sorry to have bothered you.'

'It's no bother,' the female officer said, giving her a sympathetic look. 'Take care.'

Edie waited until they'd left the courtyard before she opened her door, pushing Danny ahead of her. There was no way she intended to turn her back on him for a second.

'I'll have Mary, if it makes things easier,' James said.

He'd hung back, and she guessed he wasn't sure of her. The easiness between them had gone, replaced by awkwardness and uncertainty on both sides.

'Thank you,' she said, 'but you don't have to.'

Danny glowered at her. 'He does. He found her. I want him to have her, then I can visit her whenever I want.' He was defying her to contradict him and tell him that he couldn't see Mary. 'James, *can* I visit her?'

'That's up to your mum.'

'She said you were too busy to see us any more.'

Edie cringed. She had said that, but it was only because she couldn't tell her son the truth. He was too young to understand. She wasn't entirely certain she understood herself.

James gave her a level stare. 'She's right, I am,' he said.

'Can we talk about it?' She wanted to hear his side of the story; she'd not given him a chance to explain himself this morning.

Was it only this morning? Such a lot had happened over the course of a few hours, she felt as though the interview-that-wasn't had taken place last week.

James offered to put Mary back in her hutch while Edie got Danny ready for bed. Danny made a bit of a song and dance about wanting James to read him his bedtime story, but eventually she persuaded him to settle.

When she went downstairs it was to find James leaning against one of the kitchen worktops with a glass of wine in his hand.

'Where did that come from?' she asked, knowing full well there wasn't a drop of anything alcoholic in her house.

'I popped out to the shop on the corner. It stays open until eleven.'

'Thank you.' She took it from him and had a large mouthful. 'Thank you, too, for finding Danny.'

'You'd have found him yourself,' he assured her. 'I just happened to have a car, so was a bit quicker.'

'Anything could have happened...' She trailed off, her voice breaking, damn it; she thought she might cry again. That's all she seemed to have done today, and she was getting a bit fed up with herself for being such a wimp.

'But it didn't,' James said, 'and I don't think he'll do anything like that again. He tried not to show it, but when I pulled up next to him, he was one scared little boy. I don't think Mary was too impressed with the experience, either. Now, do you want to tell me what happened?'

When she'd finished explaining about Eastern Estates and Danny's reaction, he said, 'The offer still stands: I'll keep Mary at mine and Danny can visit any time you want. Just give me a call, and I'll come and fetch him. You too, if you want.'

He must have seen her hesitation, because he added, 'No strings. This is purely as friends. I know you said you never wanted to speak to me again…?'

'About that. I might have been a bit hasty. I still don't want your charity – but I don't think you meant it the way I took it.'

'I was only trying to help,' he said. 'I know how much working at Moira's meant to you, so when it came up for sale, I thought it might be a good idea for Julia Ferris to buy it.'

Edie blinked at him. '*Who* bought it?'

'Julia and Edgar, although you'd have been working for Julia, because I don't think Edgar has much interest in wedding dresses.'

'Julia Ferris owns Moira's?'

'Um… yeah?'

'I didn't realise. I thought…' God, she felt such an idiot.

'It makes sense,' James was saying. 'She can more or less offer a bride the complete package, from the venue, to the flowers – courtesy of Leanne – to the wedding cake – courtesy of Stevie, although that's not common knowledge yet, because she says she needs to employ another person at Peggy's before she can totally commit. And now, with the acquisition of Moira's, she can offer wedding dresses and all the gubbins that go with them.'

'Gubbins?'

'A technical term,' he said, smiling at her. 'Just out of curiosity, who did you think had bought the wedding shop?'

'You.'

'*Me?*' He began to laugh.

'What's so funny?'

'Tia told me how much her dress is costing. At those rates, I don't think I could afford to buy one of those crown things, let alone the whole shop.'

'Those crown things are called tiaras.' She paused. 'I know this is a bit forward and none of my business, but I thought you were quite rich.'

James sent her a quizzical look. 'Whatever gave you that idea?'

'Public school, the way you're such good friends with the Ferris family, that you went to Hersley Hall, and you went to London to see some earl—'

'You've got me so wrong.' His voice was soft. 'I went to public school because I was awarded a bursary, and my parents scrimped and saved for the rest. I'm only such good friends with the Ferrises because William practically adopted me. He took me under his wing and insisted I went home with him for the holidays. Julia and Edgar became an honorary aunt and uncle. And as for Hersley Hall and the Earl of Starkey, that was work. I'm as poor as the proverbial church mouse. Why do you think it's taken me this long to do the renovations on the old Hopkins place?'

'But, I thought… oh.' Edie hadn't just jumped to the wrong conclusions, she'd dived head first into them.

'Is that what this morning was about? You thought I'd bought you a shop?'

Biting her lip, Edie nodded, feeling mortified. She'd made a total and utter prat of herself.

'If I had the money, I would have done,' he murmured. 'I'd do anything to make you happy.'

'Really?'

'Really. Do you still feel that you never want to speak to me again?'

'No.' Her voice was small, but she was smiling.

'Do you want to continue with the interview?'

'Is there any point?'

'I think so, because the interview was going to consist of me telling you that Julia wants you to manage the place and you giving me a big kiss as a thank you, seeing as it was my idea for Julia to buy the shop in the first place.'

'It didn't occur to you to say anything to me? I might not have wanted the job.'

He moved towards her and her heart began to beat furiously. His gaze bore into hers, and she found herself drowning in the depth of emotion in his eyes.

Taking her in his arms, he wrapped them around her, and she melted into his solid strength.

'Tell me you don't want the job,' he teased, his lips inches from hers.

'I do want it, and not just the job. I want you, too,' she replied huskily, and she kissed him, but not before she heard his throaty chuckle as he said, 'You only want me for my money.'

Edie didn't come up for air for a very long time indeed.

Chapter 43

In the absence of any forthcoming royal nuptials, the marriage of William Ferris, the future Lord Tonbridge, to Tia Saunders, was being hailed as the wedding of the year.

Of course, Edie was invited. How could she not be, considering she'd created the dress, and she was also very publicly the best man's plus one?

Since James's revelation that Julia and Edgar Ferris had bought Moira's, things had moved swiftly, and now Edie was firmly entrenched as manager of the wedding shop. Stevie had been wonderfully understanding, and Betty had been smug and rather self-satisfied. Danny, although heartbroken that Mary had gone to live on James's smallholding, had eventually accepted the situation, which was made better by James taking her son to visit the rabbit several times a week. And, obviously, she'd felt the need to go along, too, to keep an eye on Danny – it had nothing to do with the fact that she and James spent a great deal of Danny's rabbit-visiting time kissing and canoodling while the boy was preoccupied with playing with Mary.

Edie, forever grateful to Tia for asking her to design and make a wedding dress for her (because if Tia hadn't, Edie wouldn't have met James and would have still been working for Mrs Carrington), would have closed the wedding shop today for Tia and William's wedding, if it hadn't already been shut for a revamp. Nothing major (Julia's funds wouldn't stretch that far) but Edie wanted to put her own stamp on it and bring Moira's a little more up to date. James had suggested changing the name, but both Edie and Julia had vetoed it. The shop had been built on its name, and both the manager and the owner displayed their business acumen by keeping the name exactly as it was.

Edie helped Tia dress, Tia having sent her bridesmaids out of the room beforehand, then she stood back and admired the bride.

'You look fabulous,' she declared, and was rewarded with a radiant, beaming smile.

'I'm marrying the man of my dreams and wearing the dress of my dreams,' Tia said. 'I feel like a princess.'

'That's what I was aiming for; but the dress is your vision, not mine.' She leant forward, giving the skirt a little tweak. Then she called the bridesmaids back in, and went to find her place in the ballroom, ready for the ceremony.

She was hurrying along, her heart filled with joy and thinking how absolutely wonderful Tia looked, when she rounded a corner and – oomph!

'Sorry, I— Mrs Carrington!' Edie's mouth dropped open. Her former employer was the last person she'd expected to see today.

'Edie.' Moira's mouth was its usual straight line. 'I hear you made it for her.'

'Er… yes.'

'Good. That other dress was never right.'

'It wasn't?' Edie was having trouble thinking straight.

'You knew so, otherwise why would you risk your job and go behind my back?'

Yes, why indeed…

'You're a good seamstress, you always were,' Mrs Carrington continued. 'You're an even better designer.'

Edie's mouth dropped open again; that was high praise indeed coming from her critical former boss. She was having serious difficulty believing what she was hearing.

'Before we go inside,' Mrs Carrington continued, 'I just want to say something to you.'

Edie held her breath.

'I forgive you.' Moira graciously inclined her head.

'Um, thank you?' She wasn't sure how to respond, but it wouldn't hurt to say thanks. She didn't want there to be any ill-feeling between them.

Mrs Carrington turned to enter the ballroom, and on impulse Edie caught hold of her arm. 'What about you? Are you all right?'

'Yes, my dear, I really do think I am,' she replied, then swept into the room as though she were the bride and not Tia.

Tia! Goodness, she'd better find her seat before Tia caught up with her.

As Edie entered the room, William turned around, his expression one of a rabbit caught in headlights. He looked terrified, excited and as if he was about to throw up, all at the same time. Edie gave him a reassuring smile, then her gaze found James's.

'Wow,' he mouthed at her. 'You look gorgeous.'

Edie felt gorgeous; she was wearing a dress of her own making in a pale shade of lavender, simple, yet elegant. She'd teamed it with her silver strappy sandals, silver beads in her swept-up hairdo and silver jewellery at her throat, on her wrist and in her ears.

Tia had chosen the 'Wedding March' to walk down the aisle to, and when the first notes resonated through the ballroom, everyone turned to look at the bride. Everyone except for Edie – she was more interested in the reaction of the guests. She was especially keen to see Julia's.

Lady Tonbridge was in Edie's direct line of sight, and she kept her attention on the woman's face. Her own split into a huge smile when she saw Julia's mouth drop open and her eyes widen in admiration at the first sight of Tia. There was a collective gasp of appreciation and Edie could hear several whispered comments saying how beautiful the bride looked.

Even if she didn't already know how stunning Tia looked, Edie only had to glance at William's besotted expression to see how true it was. His face was full of adoration and brimming with love, and Edie filled up with emotion at the sight of him.

She hoped that one day a man would look at her the way William was looking at his bride.

Then she met James's eye and understood that one day was today…

–

'It was a fabulous wedding,' Edie murmured several hours later as they lounged in her living room. Feeling pleasantly tired, she had her head resting against James's chest and his arm was around her waist. It wasn't often they had a Danny-free evening, and she intended to make the most of kissing and cuddling with James, but right now she was simply content to be held by him, enjoying the silence and peace after the magical, exuberant celebrations. Julia would be ecstatic at how well the wedding had gone, and Edie herself had received many compliments about Tia's dress, and even a couple of enquiries. The future of Moira's Wedding Shop looked rosy.

'It was,' he agreed, shifting slightly on the sofa, inching even closer to her. 'Have I told you how beautiful you look?'

She giggled softly. 'You have; several times.'

'I'll say it again – you're beautiful. I'm going to say something else, and I don't want you to feel you have to say anything, and I don't want to scare you off, but...' He halted, and she sat up a little, his bent head inches from hers as he drew in a deep breath then said in a rush, 'I love you. I just wanted you to know, and I don't expect anything in return, or for you to love me back, but I had to tell you how I feel about you.'

Edie's heart stopped and butterflies took flight in her tummy, shock rendering her mute. He loved her!

'I know it might be a bit soon,' he continued, 'and we haven't known each other all that long, but—'

'Shhh.' Edie wrapped her arms around his neck and lifted her chin, her lips parting. 'I love you, too. Now stop talking and kiss me.'

'There's one more thing, and this might be a bit soon, too, but I'm rattling around in that big house of mine and I thought Danny might want to see more of Mary, and now the kitchen and the bathroom are nearly done, I wondered if you'd...' He hesitated once more, biting his lip.

'Move in with you?' she finished for him, delight surging through her.

He smiled, his eyes full of love. 'I was going to say, I wondered if you'd marry me.'

Edie bit back a squeal of pure joy. 'Yes, yes, a thousand times yes!'

And all she could think about while James was kissing her soundly was that she had Tanglewood's one and only wedding shop to thank for her total and utter happiness.

Tanglewood Village series

The Tanglewood Tea Shop
The Tanglewood Flower Shop
The Tanglewood Wedding Shop